homeopathy
for the soul

By the same author:

Homeopathy in a Nutshell (Element Books)
The Tantric Sex Book

homeopathy for the soul

ways to emotional healing

CASSANDRA LORIUS

Thorsons

This book should not be used as an alternative to seeking specialist medical advice, which should be sought before any action is taken. The author and publishers cannot be held responsible for any errors and omissions that may be found in the text, or any actions that may be taken by a reader as a result of any reliance on the information contained in the text, which is taken entirely at the reader's own risk.

Thorsons
An Imprint of HarperCollins*Publishers*
77–85 Fulham Palace Road,
Hammersmith, London W6 8JB

The Thorsons website address is: www.thorsons.com

Published by Thorsons 2001

10 9 8 7 6 5 4 3 2 1

© Cassandra Lorius 2001

Cassandra Lorius asserts the moral right to
be identified as the author of this work

A catalogue record for this book
is available from the British Library

ISBN 0 7225 3929 0 (PB)
ISBN 0 00 711335 8 (HB)

Printed and bound in Great Britain by
Scotprint, Haddington

I thank all my patients for sharing their insights with me. I feel privileged to have found my vocation as a homeopath.

.

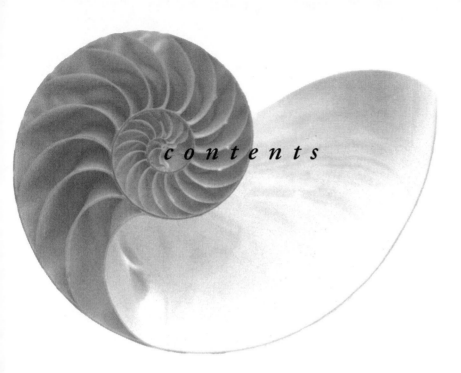

contents

Introduction xi

Part 1: Homeopathy – Medicine for the Soul
    Chapter 1:   *Soul Medicine* 3
    Chapter 2:   *The Journey Towards Cure* 26

Part 2: Preparing for Soul Work
    Chapter 3:   *Making a Start* 39
    Chapter 4:   *Different Paths of the Soul* 43
                The Path of Action 47

The Path of Experience 49

The Path of Homemaking 51

The Path of Love 54

The Path of Reparation 56

The Path of Service 58

The Path of Social Activism 60

The Path of Transcendence 62

The Path of Wisdom 65

Chapter 5: *Tracing Your Core Themes* 68

Chapter 6: *Dealing with Your Core Themes* 73

Addiction 74

Anger 78

Anxiety 82

Burnout 85

Confusion 89

Depression 93

Disease 97

Emptiness 102

Fatigue 104

Fear 107

Feeling Trapped 110

Forgiveness 113

Guilt 116

Hypersensitivity 119

Internal Conflict 122

Jealousy 125

Loneliness 127

Loss and Grief 130

Low Self-esteem 133

Oppression 136

Panic Attacks 140

Pride 143

Relationship Problems 146

Sexual Problems 150

Shock 154

Stagnation in Work 158

Workaholism 160

Part 3: Remedies for the Soul

Chapter 7: *The Remedies 165*

Aconitum Napellus 168

Anacardium 171

Arsenicum Album 175

Aurum Metallicum 180

Calcarea Carbonica 184

Causticum 187

Ignatia 190

Lachesis 195

Lycopodium 199

Medorrhinum 203

Natrum Muriaticum 206

Nux Vomica 211

Phosphorus 214

Pulsatilla 217

Sepia 221

Silica 226

Staphysagria 230

Stramonium 234

Sulphur 237

Chapter 8: *Nurturing the Soul 241*

Resources 245

Further Reading 247

Index 249

introduction

Homeopathy revolutionized my thinking when I first discovered it, and subsequently transformed my life. Since I started studying homeopathy at the age of 17, it has so radically altered the way I view the world that it is sometimes hard for me to comprehend the traditional mechanistic world view I once held, a view with which conventional medicine still identifies. According to the Greek philosopher Plato (ca 428–348 BC), physicians are misguided in considering the soul and the body as separate when treating illness. This mistake is still being made today, with modern medicine *attempting to treat the body without also paying attention to the soul. In this medical model, 'disease' is an illness that can be independently verified. In the homeopathic model, on the other hand, 'dis-ease' is a sign that the person is ill at ease in him- or herself, and that his or her soul is fragile.*

Homeopathy evolved out of a pre-biochemical view of human beings and was formulated into a coherent philosophy by German physician Samuel Hahnemann (1755–1843) in the late 18th century. In those days, all medical manuals were first and foremost healing manuals which described humans as spiritual beings with a clear purpose in life. Hahnemann tested 60 drugs from a variety of sources on himself and a small group of students. This method of testing or 'proving' substances to discover the range of symptoms they were capable of causing enabled Hahnemann to find out what they could also cure.

Having been at first seduced by and subsequently disillusioned with the conventional medical system, many of us are now rediscovering that we humans are more than just the sum of our parts. Each of us is born with our own purpose or destiny and the potential to fulfil that destiny, and it is up to us to discover and learn to develop and fulfil our potential. In the language of the respected Jungian therapist and homeopath Edward Whitmont, each of us is an acorn, with our own unique genius inspiring and guiding us. The purpose of our lives is to nurture that acorn until it grows into an oak tree.

Homeopathy is a profound energy system of medicine that cleanses and stimulates the energy system of the body – what homeopaths call the *vital force* – in order to realign a person with his or her path in life. Throughout my two decades of practice as a homeopath I have seen some of the deep transformations that homeopathy can bring about. These changes occur simultaneously on all levels of our being. Although we tend to separate out different levels of function in humans, distinguishing between body, mind and spirit, there are in fact no such distinctions or hierarchies in our being: we are composed of all of these aspects, and each affects the others. For instance, as the neurobiologist Candace Pert points out in her *Molecules of Emotion*, the components of the nervous system, the endocrine system, etc. are spread throughout the whole body rather than being localized in specific areas. Neuropeptides, the molecules of emotion, may be physical substances, but they make up our emotional chemistry; therefore, we cannot say that our emotions are separate from our bodies.

Because each of us has our own individual path in life, our personal stories are all unique. A homeopath traces the threads of our life journey to discover which remedy corresponds best to our needs. Our reaction to this individualized remedy is not perfectly predictable. It depends on the context of our own particular journey and where we are on the route, as well as on how open we are to embracing the healing energy of these remedies. I am sometimes amazed at the ways in which a remedy aligns a person with his or her own life path – that is, his or her soul's quest. By clearing obstacles that the person has encountered along the way, the remedy moves them along, helping them shape their course. The homeopathic consultation helps to unearth those deep unresolved issues, blocks, or problems that the appropriate remedy is needed to heal. As a result of my decades of experience I can chart the ways in which a homeopathic consultation restores a person to him- or herself. I know the signposts on the route, and I can share this knowledge with my patient during our follow-up discussions.

What This Book Is For

Homeopathy teaches us that, in order for a remedy to be truly holistic, the core of the person must be understood and healed. 'Feel-good' stress-management strategies or superficial alternative therapies won't get anywhere near this core! We must address the heart of each of our problems if we are going to live our lives to the full.

My thesis is simply that we are all on a spiritual path in life. The 'soul' refers to our inner essence, and it constitutes our personal connection to the spiritual realm. Our souls are in charge of what we make of our lives, even though we are not always conscious of that fact. When we go through difficult experiences without properly coming to terms with them, our responses create distortions in the energy within our bodies, like eddies in a flowing stream. These distorted patterns then influence the way we respond to situations, so that we become further entrenched in our problems and further away from our soul's purpose. If we do not deal properly with these patterns of disturbance, they will be reproduced in every aspect of our daily lives. Taking a homeopathic remedy rebalances the distorted energy pattern, freeing the soul to get on with its journey.

Homeopathy for the Soul is a book that will help you to understand the essence of your being by elucidating the heart of the homeopathic process. This process matches the energy pattern of a homeopathic remedy to the pattern created by your own energy. In order to trace your energy pattern, you need to unpick the threads running through the fabric of your life. These threads can become tight knots, restricting and binding you in a multitude of ways. Homeopathic treatment involves untying those knots, which often relate to difficult life events. Homeopathic remedies either alleviate negative emotional states, or help you to learn from and change difficult situations by viewing things from a different perspective to your habitual, damaged or pessimistic one. Our negativity often boils down to one underlying theme. If you can examine this strand and break its strangle-hold over your thought processes through homeopathy, you will be able to step into a more open space, so that you are free to explore the adventure of life in following the path of your soul. Homeopathic 'soul work' will enable you to untangle the knotted threads of your energy pattern, thereby releasing blocked energy. Once this energy starts to flow freely again, you will be able to create your personal path.

Part I of this book explores how homeopathy treats imbalances in the soul in order to cure both physical and emotional problems. The first chapter explains how homeopaths understand the soul. It explains what your energy body is, and how blockages in your energy body can cause physical and emotional symptoms. It describes how homeopathic remedies work on your energy body, clearing these blockages and thus curing these problems. I summarize what you can expect from a homeopathic consultation, and what to expect once you have been prescribed a homeopathic remedy; I also detail some of the techniques a homeopath uses to read the disturbances in your soul.

The second chapter outlines some of the different responses people have following taking a homeopathic remedy.

Part II of the book explores the things that you can do yourself to prepare for the soul work of homeopathic treatment. There is general advice about the changes you can make in your life to increase your level of energy (Chapter 3). The next two chapters (4 and 5) feature two techniques that you can use to find out more about your own energy pattern and where it may be unbalanced or stuck. The first of these chapters suggests how you can discover your own spiritual path in life. The second explains how you can trace the recurring psychological problems that form the core themes which lie behind the physical and emotional symptoms you face. The final chapter in this part (Chapter 6) takes each of these psychological problems and details how homeopathy understands and treats them.

Part III of the book contains profiles of a selection of the homeopathic remedies commonly used for treating emotional problems. Within Chapter 7, for each remedy I describe the energy pattern of people who would benefit from the remedy, what you can expect should you take it, and a 'soul-learning' – advice about the possible realization open to you if you are in a situation corresponding to the remedy's energy pattern. This section will give readers a good understanding of the range and depth of homeopathic remedies, and encourage them to think through complex issues on a deep level in order to prepare themselves for a visit to a homeopath. The final chapter of the book (Chapter 8) invites readers to consider some suggestions about ways to nurture the soul.

Throughout the book I illustrate what I am saying with brief sketches of the cases of people who have consulted me for homeopathic treatment.

This book will encourage readers to evaluate their own life stories and current self-perceptions, and to try to discover the central issue blocking them from progressing. However, because there are usually a number of issues to be addressed, as well as the presence of physical conditions that need to be considered, and because it is often difficult to evaluate the effects of a remedy, I recommend that readers also seek the expertise of a professional homeopath, whether the issue seems self-evident or complex. The topics highlighted in this book provide a means of working on oneself by observing and articulating the core issues that need to be resolved. This is the first step in making transformations. Visiting a professional homeopath is the next important step on that path.

My Story

I first discovered the power of an alternative approach to healing through personal experience. When I was four years old my stepfather suffered psychiatric symptoms after a mental breakdown. His frequent crises involved regular hospitalization, where he was variously prescribed drugs, electric-shock treatment or psychotherapy. None of these interventions had any impact on the natural periodic pattern of his psychosis: they just dulled the intensity of his experiences or substituted a different kind of hell for the one in which he was living at the time. Finally my mother took him to see a Chinese acupuncturist, which was to prove a turning point for my stepfather's state of mind. The transformation was so impressive that my mother then started training to be an acupuncturist, when I was 13.

For me, coming to homeopathy was not this kind of conversion experience; rather, it appealed to me intellectually, as acupuncture did not. I saw acupuncture as being framed by a radically different cultural experience and steeped in thousands of years of history that I did not share.

I was lucky to find my calling at the early age of 17. I realized how lucky I was only after meeting numerous people who had spent decades searching for work that was fulfilling and meaningful. Studying homeopathy was like a love affair for me, with an instant attraction that deepened as its philosophical shape was revealed. The homeopathic world view resonated with me more and more, shaping my reality throughout my adult life.

I graduated from the College of Homeopathy in London in 1979. I first saw the depths to which homeopathy could work during my postgraduate studies with the world-renowned homeopath George Vithoulkas, author of the seminal work, *The Science of Homeopathy*. I spent several years studying with him, both at seminars around Europe and on a two-year training programme in London, where I was part of a group of dedicated homeopaths who brought George our challenging cases for him to treat, giving us the opportunity to analyse his approach while watching the cases unfold over time.

As well as inspiring me as a teacher, George also prescribed a 'constitutional' remedy for me that was to have profound repercussions on the course of my life (see page 18). Like most patients, I was not aware of the profundity of these changes until they were well underway. After the first dose of my constitutional remedy, Kali Iodatum, I went through an intense physical reaction during which some of my physical complaints worsened; reactions of this kind are termed *aggravations* (see page 32). It was only after this physical reaction subsided that I became aware of the more subtle effects of the remedy on my sorely depleted energy body, and yet more months before the remedy had mustered the energy resources to begin to develop a more nourishing life for me. This whole sequence took at least two years to unfold. The remedy enabled me to make important psychological and practical changes in my life, helping me to move through my inner obstacles to expressing my passions. The changes I made in my life led to a multitude of new openings. In particular, I finished an unsatisfactory relationship, met my biological father for the first time, and eventually went to live in Egypt for a year – a life-affirming experience that improved my confidence.

The realization that I was on the right path was heralded by a series of profound dreams, which I describe in a section on responses to my 'constitutional' remedy (see page 19). Within weeks I found myself writing for a Cairo magazine and working at a well-equipped hospital with a wonderful woman doctor who became my translator and co-adventurer. Out of that experience came many others: I started a homeopathic training programme in Egypt, and did more and more writing. Egypt turned out to be a long love affair, a magical experience that showed me the resources I had inside and taught me to pay attention to my deepest desires. As I recall the New Age author Deepak Chopra saying, your desires are the seeds of intention, and, by formulating your intention, you allow things to manifest themselves. His words have stayed with me.

When I came back from Egypt at the end of that year, I realized that I loved working as a homeopath, but I had misgivings about the pace at which I was working. Dealing with people's problems full-time was just too much; I wanted to do other things in my spare time as well. In particular, I wanted to carry on writing, studying and learning. I discuss my problems at this period in more detail in the section on burnout (see page 85).

Reading Lawrence Le Shan's inspirational book *Cancer as a Turning Point*, I was struck by the fact that all the people he writes of in this book had to go through the ordeal of cancer before they could give themselves permission to do what they really wanted to do without worrying about the consequences. Only then did they start living as if that day, week, or month was to be their last. One bought a motorbike and drove off into the sunset, another started training as an opera singer; all did whatever it was they had always dreamed of doing but had dismissed as too far-fetched. On reading these stories I asked myself, 'What is it I want to do that I have not done?'

The answer came to me on a beach in Cornwall, near Land's End, at the southernmost tip of England, a place to which I often went to take stock and find inspiration. It was 'Go to university.' I was surprised: it was not the answer I expected. I came back to London and applied to my chosen university, The School of Oriental and African Studies. I was accepted despite a number of bureaucratic obstacles, and subsequently spent four exciting years studying social anthropology. It was wonderful to be doing something that was just for me, although in some ways it felt indulgent because it did not seem to be linked to my working life. It enriched me enormously by producing yet another shift in my world view, widening the individual frame of homeopathy into a broader social perspective, and showing me yet again, in different ways, how relative our personal beliefs are, and how much our views really do shape the world we live in.

Through anthropology I came to understand more deeply the ways in which we determine our own life stories, and how we tend to limit ourselves with our blind belief that this is the only way things can be. Living with such limitations usually cramps our character and creates the kinds of personality distortions and emotional disturbances we can see in those people we know to be unfulfilled.

What I have learned through my own experience is that you sometimes have to be selfish in order to grow. You have to be true to yourself and your deeper needs if you are to explore your potential fully. This is not a superficial egotistic selfishness, although it can seem like that when you are talking about throwing in your job and expecting your dependents to adapt to your change in circumstances. It does not mean living your life without compromise, since every relationship is a matter of negotiation and flexibility. However, in doing what you really want and need to do, you can give more to others. If you are fulfilled and happy, you have more resources to draw on than if you are frustrated, resentful or bitter about your lot in life.

I try to keep these thoughts in mind as I learn more, through parenting, about the meaning of the word 'service'. The last time I looked inside myself to find out what deep desires I harboured, I discovered my wish to have children. Mothering has been an opening for me, allowing me to experience and express the most loving feelings in abundance.

Our spiritual paths are as unique to us as our personal histories. They are all about our attempts to allow more of the soul to be felt and seen in our daily lives. To me, living with an awareness of soul means having meaning and depth in what I am doing in life. I feel more in touch with my soul when I am doing something I feel passionate about, as well as when I'm with my lover, or in nature.

When I was about seven, my family lived in an untouched place in the north island of New Zealand, miles away from other habitations. That experience has left me with a love of being in nature and a need to sit in silence. Some people know themselves and their desires through talking or expressing them in other ways. I need to go quietly inside myself to uncover something that is emerging, and then nurture it. I see practices like meditation and dance as ways of creating a window on the soul.

Throughout my life I have been aware of a spiritual searching. This has led me to a number of experiences and teachers. Through my deep interest in Sufism (the mystical branch of Islam), I opened up to the spiritual dimensions of love, and through Tantra (a pre-Hindu esoteric tradition) I discovered a way of applying that love to an intimate relationship. I am attracted to these mystical traditions because they emphasize opening your heart. On the path of the heart (see page 54), the capacity to love is paramount. My natural zest for life and engagement with others serves me on this path, while my strong emotions and passionate nature have created a romantic disposition with a need for close and loving relationships. However, according to the Dalai Lama, the spiritual head of Tibetan Buddhism, too much focus on a primary relationship can be detrimental to further spiritual development. The homeopathic remedy that George Vithoulkas prescribed for me was instrumental in healing a lot of the hurt and disappointment I had experienced as a result of investing too much in my relationships with men. I am still exploring my own path and redefining it as I go along.

I would like to encourage you to find your own path and discover how to express the things that you feel passionate about. I intend this book as an invitation to you to discover what makes your heart sing.

part 1

homeopathy –
medicine for the soul

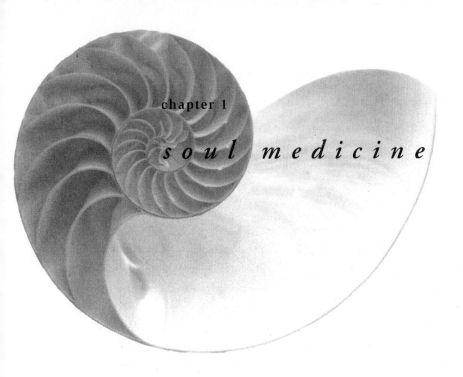

soul medicine

Homeopathy and the Soul

The core of your humanity is in the area of your will, under-standing and heart – all attributes of what the ancient sages called the soul. According to the homeopath Martin Miles, the path to healing involves integrating these different faculties of the soul; it means reconciling your intentions with your actions, your wishes with your will, and what you are with what you would like to be. The path to healing involves striv-ing to bring all the aspects of your life into an integrated relationship. For me, once I had recognized that I was drawn toward the path of love, I realized that I had to nurture my caring and compassionate qualities in order to balance my strong mind with an awareness of the importance of the wisdom of the heart.

The way I understand the concept of 'soul' is that it is our personal connection to the spiritual dimension, while our personality is more a reflection of our ego. By 'ego' I mean the psychoanalytic term, which refers to our personal identity in the world. We can nurture our soul through fostering our awareness of the realm of the spirit (see Chapter 8); otherwise it can waste away, according to the choices we make about the manner in which we live our life. Once you become aware of your soul, you need to live in accordance with its needs.

Aligning your soul to the world of spirit rather than to the world of the personal ego and materialism can be challenging, because it requires you to be conscious of your actions and intentions and to overcome the resistance, inertia and selfishness of an ego-centred perspective. As individuals, we do need a strong ego or sense of self to cope with the demands in our pressured lives, but a conscious awareness of its limits can help the soul express its work.

The physical body is vital to manifesting the purpose of our soul. It is through our bodies that we find ways to express a personal vision in life. Each of us has something unique to contribute to our fellow beings: we just need to clear our energy bodies so that our soul can shine forth. Homeopathic remedies can help us do just that.

Martha's case is a good example of how homeopathic treatment heals both physical and emotional problems, and validates a more spiritual side to life.

Martha struggled with feelings of grief and anger that she tried to suppress, although she acknowledged that they fuelled her political activism. Her political anger was grounded in her own experience of suffering. She had hated being pitied and felt humiliated at the poverty of her childhood. Activism also provided a means to finding a similarly motivated peer group, although personal emotions were considered marginal in the political arena.

Martha had been campaigning for local government for many years, driven by a sense of idealism that was gradually disappointed by the political climate of the Conservative national government. She had originally consulted me for homeopathic treatment because of her chronic arthritis, bladder infections and menopausal symptoms, but what emerged as equally important was her sense of disillusion and frustration.

Under homeopathic treatment with the remedy Causticum (see page 187), Martha was able to let go of her now redundant identity as a local government activist and to use her experience constructively to look at how her whole peer group was affected by the changing political climate. She began to find her inner sense of authority, which encouraged her to take the risk of speaking about subjects that she had previously assumed no one was interested in. The Causticum helped give Martha the confidence she needed to break her habitual silence by writing about the personal side of her political involvement in various journals, and she also started the painful task of recalling early childhood griefs that she had tried to bury as an adult. For the first time she was able to explore her feminine, maternal and sexual roles – all areas she had felt she had to ignore over the previous few decades in order to be accepted within the political culture she had aligned herself to.

Martha attributes the reawakening of her spiritual consciousness to her recovery. She said, 'There was always a bit of me that hung on to a spiritual way of thinking even though this was very embarrassing to admit to in the circles I moved in. It was as if I lived in split worlds, and it made me very anxious about revealing myself. Accepting and understanding the depth and importance of what I call emotional thinking has been a revelation for me.

'It's only in the last two years since I've been using homeopathy that I've begun to understand what "being" is. Instead of always trying to find a million solutions for everything, I can just listen. This has brought me much closer to my children. I really regret the fact that when they were younger I spent all my time *doing* things for them instead of just spending time *being* together.'

Homeopathy and the Energy Body

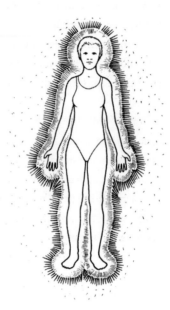

The energy body

Although most people come to a homeopath because of medical problems, what they really need is help to connect with their inner essence in order to heal their distorted energy bodies.

Your energy creates a field around your body, which psychically receptive people can see as your aura. Your physical body is both a template for your energy body and a manifestation of it. Whether energy flows freely or not in your body determines the way you act in the world. When you get stuck in a particular stance or attitude to life, the energy that normally flows freely through the energy body becomes blocked in certain areas and stagnates. Diseases can be a concrete manifestation of this stagnation. Because homeopaths believe that we are pure energy, they prescribe energy medicine to treat us in the form of homeopathic remedies. Each remedy is specially prepared to work on our energy body.

Our individual energy field forms a pattern in which distinct threads can be traced. Because your responses reflect the state of your energy field, an experienced homeopath can glimpse the pattern behind your behaviour. The art of homeopathy is the art of matching the energy patterns of remedies, as I will describe in the remedy profiles in Part III, with those of our energy bodies.

Often one fundamental theme can be identified in a person's energy pattern which manifests itself in his or her responses to a wide range of everyday situations.

Katy was a young girl who felt abandoned as a result of her parents' separation and had become extremely attached to her mother. Her constant need to know where her mother was at any given moment affected every situation she encountered. If she saw a trail of ants, her first concern was to wonder where their mother was. When playing games with her friends, her first question was who would play the mother. The energy pattern behind her behaviour matched that of the remedy Pulsatilla (see page 217). It helped her feel more secure and independent of her mother, and healed her sense of abandonment.

Sometimes disturbances in our energy body are the result of our parents' experience rather than our own, and for children it is often connected with the mother's situation during pregnancy. Homeopaths believe that, like personality traits, soul qualities can be handed down through the generations. You can carry your parents' qualities of integrity or sensitivity within you, as well as their fears and unresolved problems. Homeopathy is unique in having remedies that can deal with generational patterns of trauma, which homeopathy terms 'miasmatic'. Homeopathic remedies clear a way for the soul to incarnate properly, helping children to throw off the legacy of their parents' problems and come into their own lives more fully.

Tom's mother was pregnant with him during the Second World War. Because of her intense claustrophobia, she preferred to crouch under the kitchen table rather than go into an air-raid shelter during bomb attacks on London. Within the first month of his life Tom was separated from his mother when she became ill with scarlet fever. He had been shy and introverted as a child and began to stammer from the age of three.

Later, in 1971, Tom developed manic depression, regularly going into egotistical states where he was full of inflated ideas about his own importance and capacities. His tremendous success in business had made him feel powerful, intelligent and in charge of his life. However, he would get increasingly loquacious and manic and then flip into a period of paranoia. He was treated with anti-psychotic medications for 12 years. His consultant neurologist explained that the high doses of lithium carbonate may have eventually damaged Tom's cerebellum, producing 'multi-system atrophy', a state which left him severely disabled in walking, speaking and in other basic physical functions.

He was prescribed the remedy Stramonium (see page 234) because of his mother's terror about survival while he was in the womb. This theme seemed to have been played out in his early childhood experiences of insecurity and separation. Homeopaths see stammering as a sign that children are frightened. As an adult Tom had developed egotistical strategies to compensate for his earlier experiences of insecurity, but, because of his fundamentally fragile sense of self, his psychological state had become extremely unbalanced.

Under treatment with Stramonium over some years, Tom has become much more physically mobile and, more importantly, he has regained his creative fluency which he expresses through writing, publishing and giving public readings of his poetry. He set up a poetry group, aptly named Survivors' Poetry for survivors of mental distress. He has had no further bouts of either mania or depression since he started homeopathic treatment in 1986.

Jim and Ursula's second baby was stillborn, and although they felt ready to have another baby they suffered intense grief throughout the third pregnancy. When their daughter was born she was very unsettled and couldn't be comforted, which, in the absence of other reasons, I presumed was a result of the trauma she had inherited from her parents. I gave her a dose of Ignatia. She responded well: her mood became much more calm and settled, and she slept better.

The reason I chose Ignatia (see page 190) was that this remedy matched the energy pattern of the emotional trauma which her parents were immersed in at the time of her conception and which they had passed on to their new baby. I treated the parents with Ignatia as well in order to heal this grief and enable the family feel close and secure in spite of their loss. The parents' pervasive sorrow had affected their first-born child also, but in a different way. He developed a repetitive cough and became unusually quiet. I chose a different homeopathic remedy for him, Silica (see page 226), because he reacted to feeling insecure by becoming increasingly sensitive, shy and introverted.

How Remedies Work on the Energy Body

Remedies have a dynamic effect on the energy body of the person taking them. They release the knots in the energy field and allow the energy to flow unimpeded once again. Homeopathic remedies seem to clear these blockages through a process of amplification. This is the idea behind the fundamental homeopathic principle that 'like cures like': that is, that two similar energy patterns will harmonize each other. The remedy focuses the body's healing resources on the knot, providing the impetus for the energy body to release it.

Once the energy disturbance in an individual has been healed, other symptoms of imbalance, whether physical or emotional, will normally resolve themselves. Therefore, experienced homeopaths tend not to pay as much attention to physical symptoms as to other signs of imbalance in the energy body, because of our observation that any problems with physical function sort themselves out once the energy body is rebalanced.

Jenny was plagued with genital warts. She had returned countless times to the hospital clinic over the years to have the warts burned off, but they would always quickly return in greater numbers, until she had dozens of them. She came to me in despair, and was amazed when all the warts disappeared after only two or three treatments with homeopathy. I had prescribed the remedy Staphysagria (see page 230), primarily because of her frustration about her unhappy sexual relationships, which seemed to be at the core of her problems. After treatment, Jenny decided to extricate herself from the unsatisfying and obsessive relationship she was embroiled in.

Homeopathy is an 'energy' system of medicine, based on a model of the human which includes an energy field or 'vital force'. We know from modern physics that our seemingly solid bodies are just dense fields of energy. A disturbance in our energy field can give rise to disease, while a potent form of energy can rebalance us. Homeopathy uses 'potentized' remedies to rebalance our body's subtle energy body. Once this is back in balance, everything is able to function better.

Homeopathic remedies treat only distortions in the energy pattern. While negative states of mind and ways of behaving can restrict your creative expression, positive feelings are a natural manifestation of the soul. Remedies can only enhance the positive aspects of your particular energy pattern – they don't diminish those aspects. Their therapeutic effects are primarily concerned with healing the damaging residues of negative emotions and unresolved situations.

Sally came to see me when she was seven months pregnant, anxious about issues of life and death. Her brother-in-law had been killed in an accident just a few days after his daughter was born, and this had cast a shadow over the coming birth of her own baby. Sally's father had also died earlier that year, and all these losses restimulated her sadness about her much-loved first husband, who had died of cancer. She had recovered and gone on to create another family, but, in some ways, the fact that things were going so well for her made her feel guilty. Sally found it difficult to enjoy her happiness, especially when she saw her sister struggling with being alone.

I gave Sally the remedy Natrum muriaticum (page 206), because of the way her reaction to all the loss around her made her feel as if she had to keep her emotions to herself. She always felt that she had to put others' needs before hers. Sometimes Sally felt she couldn't cope with hearing about other people's problems, yet she berated herself for not being even more supportive towards her sister. The remedy enabled her to heal her grief and prepared her to rejoice at the arrival of her new baby without guilt or anguish.

Emotional Healing

Many of our physical and psychological symptoms result from compensatory strategies which we develop in trying to deal with difficult feelings such as anxiety and tension, shocks, disappointments and losses. Although these strategies initially allow us to cope with intense feelings, eventually they can become blocks to our emotional growth and psychological health. In his book *Emotional Healing with Homeopathy*, Peter Chappell has described how energy can be dammed up by traumatic experiences, obstructing the vital flow of energy.

I experienced this myself most forcefully among the Palestinians I worked with in Cairo. Many of them were suffering from chronic psychological symptoms as a result of the experiences they had been through of warfare, torture, displacement and loss.

Naima came to see me because her periods had ceased nearly a year earlier. It emerged that she suffered from an intense phobia about germs, which led to her washing her hands frequently throughout the day. The fear of contamination made her extremely apprehensive about the thought of having to have sexual relations with a man, and this apprehension had caused her to cancel two engagements already. She had recently become engaged again, but felt increasingly anxious about the thought of going through with the marriage. Because of the way the tremendous insecurity she had experienced throughout her childhood had resulted in Naima developing neurotic fears, I prescribed the remedy Arsenicum album, which reinstated her menstrual cycle and alleviated her anxiety state, enabling her to go through with the wedding.

We may try to cope with difficult feelings by splitting them off from the rest of ourselves. When we do this, part of us moves forward while the other part digs its heels in and resists. This can make us feel scared or stuck, or sometimes just numb. The negative experiences which we attempt to split off from our core are actually the very things we need to come to terms with in order to heal and move on in life. Even if we realize that this is true, staying in a familiar situation can seem more comfortable, even if it makes you feel stuck, frustrated or depressed, than taking the risk of following an opening through the maze and out into the light. In order to motivate yourself to get out of such a situation, you first need to untangle the threads that bind you and keep you in a state of inertia.

People sometimes comment hopelessly that they do not expect remedies to help them, because they are stuck in the poverty trap, in an untenable marriage or on their own with young children. But we all know from countless anecdotes how the indomitable spirit can find hope and faith even in the most horrendous situations. Homeopathic remedies help to break up the way your energy is blocked by hopelessness and negativity, and allow your fundamental optimism to reveal itself.

In *The Spirit of Homeopathy* Dr Rajan Sankaran describes remedies as 'situational'. In other words, the symptom picture pointing to the remedy you need is produced by the situation you are stuck in. For instance, if you feel stuck in a situation that you can not change, you might respond by feeling angry or trapped, or by feeling oppressed (see Chapter 6, page 136). If you respond by feeling trapped, for instance, this can further shape the way you view your life, unconsciously reinforcing the situation. To encourage you to keep an open mind, I suggest that whenever you feel trapped you consider whether you can use your circumstances as a learning opportunity to understand how you yourself may have contributed to this feeling of entrapment. That's why, in the chapter on dealing with your core themes (Chapter 6) I suggest a possible 'soul lesson' for each of the situations I describe.

Homeopathic remedies can change your perception of your situation and allow you to feel a greater sense of personal freedom, even if you cannot change the practical conditions of your life. In this way remedies can help you to deal with even the most entrenched and seemingly insoluble situations.

Lawrence was an actor who had had to change career after his stage fright got so bad that he began to stammer. He had become very introverted in spite of his intensely emotional nature, and had never been able to form a sexual relationship. This started after his mother died, leaving him living alone in her house. He had always experienced a feeling of detachment from others and said that his mother rejected him as a young baby, when her husband disappeared. 'When I'm under a lot of stress I think I can't cope any longer and I'm afraid of cracking up,' he told me.

His mother's death revealed how isolated and lonely Lawrence felt, but instead of suffering a mental breakdown he was able to turn his affliction into a source of consolation. After a time, Lawrence became a successful mime artist and entertainer, surrounding himself with an atmosphere of conviviality by giving other people pleasure. As his self-confidence improved after taking the remedy Mercurius solubilis, he stopped stammering. He then realized that he'd been hiding behind his successful career persona and needed to improve his social life by exposing the real person behind the mask. The remedy gave him the courage to embark on making friendships and building the foundations necessary for nurturing close relationships.

Dealing with stress in any form has the potential to destabilize us, throwing up conflict and change which can bring us to question the purpose of life. Whether a growing awareness of lack of fulfilment is experienced as a crisis or a quest depends on our internal resources. This awareness can signal a need to change our priorities. But if we feel threatened, we are thrown into crisis. For instance, feelings of pointlessness can surface if any of the socially accepted signs of external success, such as a job or material possessions, disappear. Feelings of helplessness or hopelessness can then threaten to overwhelm us. These feelings are often the hallmark of depression. A homeopathic remedy can deal with the depression, allowing you to reconstruct your identity in affirmative ways. This is a more healthy response to the challenge of your changing circumstances.

Ruth came to see me suffering from severe depression after her lover's father had died and a friend had been killed in an accident. Soon afterwards she had lost her job and became so depressed that she was scarcely able to get up in the morning. Psychotherapy was not helping her. She did not want to see anyone and she could barely speak. She said, 'I can see the words but I can't actually say them. I can hardly think and I feel so tired that I could die. Everything feels too much and little irritations make me wild with anger. I had to finish my relationship because I had nothing at all to give emotionally.'

Her feelings had become walled up behind a defeated reaction to the losses in her life that dulled her thoughts, numbed her and made it difficult for her to give or receive love. She no longer knew what she wanted or needed, and she felt a terrible sense of isolation. She experienced a dramatic and lasting improvement on taking the remedy Natrum muriaticum (see page 206), which I gave her because of the way she pushed away those people who were close to her when she could no longer cope with her depression.

Like Ruth, many people find that psychotherapy alone cannot cure depression. Psychotherapy may help you to become consciously aware of the state you are in, and it may be able to help you understand its causes, but often this is not enough. Other people experience the limitations of some psychotherapeutic approaches which risk identifying them even more deeply with their neuroses and leave them stuck in their pain. Homeopathic remedies can work well alongside psychotherapy by enabling you to let go of the emotional and spiritual blocks revealed by the process of therapy. Homeopathic remedies release these blocks, allowing you to benefit a lot more from the process of therapy.

A measure of your level of health or sickness is the degree to which you can be fully present in the moment, responding to what is happening around you without prejudice. Brooding over past situations constricts and stops you from living in the present. The appropriate homeopathic remedy provides an impulse to change these unhealthy patterns, making space for a new experience of yourself. It enables you to uncover what is already there: your true potential.

Nadia, a woman of 41, came for homeopathic treatment during a long mid-life crisis which manifested itself through depression, as well as unexplained neurological symptoms which were very painful and frightening. A barrage of medical tests could not provide an explanation, so she was forced to find her own ways of managing her problems.

Every area of her life seemed unresolved. Her partner didn't want a baby and their sex life had virtually ceased. She hated her work although she was afraid to resign and pursue a living making music, which was her real passion. 'A lack of confidence has always held me back, and I've always needed mentors to encourage me through their faith in me.'

I prescribed the remedy Causticum (see page 187) because of Nadia's strong sense of integrity and the way she had used her job as a vehicle to express her commitment to social justice. The point when she was personally attacked as a result of internal politics in the workplace was the point where she lost her commitment to that way of furthering the cause. After three years of 'angsting', Nadia suddenly decided to leave work. After handing in her notice she experienced a surge of energy which made her elated and, at times, euphoric. There was not a moment's doubt in her mind about her decision and she was no longer riddled with uncertainty about whether she could support herself by working freelance. Her partner offered to support her, and their relationship became much closer.

'My task now is to be my own inner mentor,' Nadia told me. She felt a tremendous sense of excitement even as she commenced a lot of soul searching about how to shape her new life, because it was apparent that the future would hold many surprises as well as challenges.

The Principles of Homeopathy

There are over 3,000 homeopathic remedies. They come from a wide range of sources. Homeopathic preparations contain infinitesimal amounts of the original substance, whether this is something poisonous such as deadly nightshade (Belladonna) or something innocuous like salt (Natrum muriaticum). To make the six centesimal potency of Arsenicum album 6c, for example, one part of arsenic is added to 99 parts of milk, sugar or alcohol and 'succussed' (shaken vigorously). This process is then repeated six times. The number on the label of a homeopathic remedy tells you how many dilutions it has gone through. A 30 centesimal potency has gone through the same process of dilution 30 times. Although a 30 has been diluted more than a 6, the increased number of succussions has made it more powerful, so it will usually be taken for more serious problems than a 6 potency would be taken for.

Remedies can also be diluted according to the decimal scale: that is, one part to nine. In this case there will be an *x* next to the number (e.g. 6x). Hahnemann also devised a third scale, the LM scale, in which remedies are diluted one part to a thousand.

What makes a medicine homeopathic is not how it is made, however, but whether it is used according to the *principles* of homeopathy. A remedy will work only if it fits the picture produced by the whole of the disturbed energy body. Whereas the term 'holistic medicine' has become somewhat meaningless as a result of being applied indiscriminately to successive 'latest' therapeutic techniques, homeopathy is holistic in the true sense. During a homeopathic consultation signs of imbalance on all levels of the person's being are discussed: physical symptoms, emotional states, mental problems and spiritual issues. All of these are originally produced by imbalance in the energy body and make up a coherent picture of the state that needs a single homeopathic remedy. The appropriate homeopathic remedy to untangle the picture is the one that best corresponds to this whole state.

The word *homeopathy* comes from the Greek for 'similar suffering'. This reflects the key philosophic principle behind the homeopathic method: a substance can cure the very suffering it is capable of causing.

There are three fundamental principles of homeopathy:

- 'Like cures like.' Remedies cure the patterns of disturbance in an unhealthy person that they are capable of causing when tested on a well person. A homeopath matches the right remedy picture with the symptoms that need treating. These symptoms are the threads of disturbance at the core of your being. Both physical and psychological symptoms are important as well as spiritual issues.
- 'The minimum dose'. A homeopath will prescribe the least amount of medicine needed to get you back on the right track. Classical homeopaths usually use a single dose of only one remedy in high potency to treat problems at a soul level. This remedy is known as your 'constitutional remedy'.
- 'The process of cure'. Following natural laws that have been formulated as a result of observing how deep healing takes place, a homeopath will treat more serious problems before less serious ones. Treating the core of your problem is better than treating the physical symptoms. As physical problems are the result of an energetic disturbance, this means treating the fundamental disturbance in your energy body first.

A Homeopathic Consultation

For me, a homeopathic consultation is about trying to tune in to the movements of someone's soul, rather than trying to give advice or impose a solution. It is important not to be in a hurry to offer an opinion. I believe that you cannot tell the soul what to do: you can only offer it an opportunity to do the necessary work itself by providing resources in the medium of the remedy. The homeopathic remedy can create an opportunity that the soul utilizes even when the person is not conscious of what needs to be done in terms of practical change. I have realized that you cannot alter a person's ways just by talking: it is the remedy that will facilitate transformation to occur in a person's soul. Nevertheless, the alert, active attention that a homeopath can provide as a person tells his or her life story is the first step in the process of healing.

In order to see the workings of the soul beneath people's personality traits, I create an atmosphere of attentive awareness, which allows them to tell me how they view their health and their life. The stories people narrate help the homeopath uncover the precise remedy needed for deep healing.

The way I work is very much influenced by my teacher, George Vithoulkas. I found his approach to eliciting the inner truth from patients inspirational, and his style resonated with my own ability to encourage people to open up. From him I discovered that the hunt for the precious nuggets of information which homeopaths traditionally use as flags to indicate the most appropriate remedy for a person is not the most important thing. What is crucial is to create an atmosphere for patients to settle into storytelling mode, to talk honestly and self-reflectively about their lives. Active listening, which involves paying attention not only to the words people say but also the way they are said, as well as to what else might be unsaid, has given me the privilege of sharing insights with others.

I asked Cathy, a woman I have been seeing for over a decade, to describe my approach. Cathy told me that she often feels challenged by the questions I ask and by the comments I make on her narrative, because I invite her to look at what is going on in her life from the perspective of her higher self. Cathy finds that with me she can expose her vulnerability and the places where she feels disempowered in her life.

It is important to be accepted without being judged. This role as a witness allows people to let go of their defensive strategies and drop down deeper into their own being, contacting the soul. Doing this allowed Cathy to transform her problems. She described the effect of seeing me as 'like shining a light into the future'.

This mutual attentive engagement with a person's life experiences enables him or her to clarify core issues and access deeper insights. Once the core themes have been excavated, the homeopath can turn his or her attention to matching the pattern displayed by the imbalanced energy to the patterns of homeopathic remedies. The pattern of imbalanced energy usually contains lots of different knots, but homeopaths search to find the fundamental issue that makes sense of the whole pattern. Once unknotted, all the other inter-connected threads will also smooth out.

In constitutional treatment, a homeopath explores all of your symptoms, including any emotional and mental changes, and makes an assessment of your individual constitution and any imbalances it may have. A remedy closely matching all these aspects of your condition is then prescribed.

A detailed model has been developed by master homeopath George Vithoulkas which allows us to understand the correlation of symptoms and to identify their underlying cause. Homeopathy seeks to treat this core problem from which the symptoms stem. Only when this fundamental problem is sorted out can your energy levels improve and your physical symptoms be cured.

In *constitutional treatment*, the homeopath chooses a single remedy, selected to match the energy pattern of the person as expressed by the core of their being. The potency or strength of the remedy is selected to match the depth of the disorder in the individual.

Reading the Soul

In homeopathic consultations, people tell many different types of story, which allow me to read the patterns of their souls. I listen to what they have to tell me of their level of energy, their spiritual direction and their psychological and physical symptoms. Sometimes the most revealing clues about the state of the soul stem from experiences for which there is no rational explanation. These include gut reactions, strong, unexplained impulses and the messages found in our dreams. These experiences alert us to a different sort of intelligence to that which is accessible through the intellect.

Being drawn to live in Egypt changed the course of my life. I first went there on holiday. One day, my friend and I went into a shop to purchase a piece of lapis lazuli. The man who ran the shop turned out to be a healer, and before we knew it he had asked us to meditate on the various gems he had collected. We spent a few days with him, discussing dreams and meditating, and it was then that Egypt started to work its magic on me. I decided to follow the strong impulse this encounter awakened in me to live in Egypt. I now see that the time I spent living there was one of the most important periods in my life.

Dreams also give us a glimpse of the patterns in our souls. Homeopath and Jungian therapist Edward Whitmont describes dreams as allegorical statements about the psychic energy patterns relevant to our current situation. They are also significant in heralding inner transformations. They can be used as a guide to the subtle changes going on in our energy bodies.

Chloe repeatedly has detailed, wondrous dreams of snakes. Since the provings of homeopathic remedies include taking account of recurrent themes in dreams, her dreams of snakes provided one of the indicators for giving her the homeopathic remedy, Lac caninum. Another remedy that is indicated by dreams of snakes is Lachesis (see page 195), which is prepared from the bushmaster snake.

Snakes traditionally represent the powerful energetic forces in our body, visualized as a coiled serpent in the reservoir of personal energy at the base of the spine, and called kundalini by the Hindus. These snake remedies are connected very much with stepping into one's personal power. They are also about feeling at ease with sexual energy and using it to power other areas in our lives, integrating the primal sexual energy with other aspects of the energy body.

Chloe's internal state is illustrated in her dreams by the appearance and context of the snakes: sometimes they are small and unthreatening, sometimes frightening, and at other times ambiguous. To me they represent her relationship with her own energy source, something that is difficult for her to inhabit fully because she feels contaminated by the energy field of her controlling mother. Her path to healing involved distancing herself from her mother's need to dominate, and laying claim to her own powerful feminine energy.

The remedy made Chloe feel much stronger, as a result of being able to experience herself in a new way without feeling overwhelmed. Since she is an artist with a strongly developed creative side, I suggested that she also use some of the rich images from her dream life as creative visualizations to work with the changes brought about by her remedy. These provided her with a way of separating herself from the intense emotional demands of her mother, which she experienced as if they were in her own body. One powerful image we shared was of the consuming mother as a vast black raven struggling out of a physical body – a sure sign of psychic separation taking place.

By interpreting my own dreams I have been able to tell whether or not I have been on the right path in my life. After the 'constitutional' homeopathic remedy given to me by my teacher George Vithoulkas, I could tell I was on a path of transformation because of a series of profound dreams. They started a couple of months after I had taken the remedy, when I was in Turkey with a friend, Eileen, exploring a ruined healing temple dedicated to the ancient Greek god of medicine, Asclepius. In ancient times patients would come to this temple to be healed, and they slept overnight in its circular chambers. On waking, their dreams would be interpreted and the meaning of their symptoms divined, and the treatment required then fell into place. Eileen and I dozed off in a dream chamber in the afternoon sun. After waking in a daze, quietly looking at the grassy knolls over the deserted ruins of the temple grounds, the image of a large seed encased in a thick, pithy, hairy skin came to me. In the same instant the seed jumped out of its pod into my mouth, and I swallowed it, symbolically incorporating the seed into my body.

Over the next few days I pondered the significance of this symbol, but my intellect could not find a neat analysis. Instead I experienced its meaning as a tremendous surge of energy that impelled me to make a rapid succession of changes in my life. The energy released was so intense that at times I found myself whirling around like a dervish in the living room of a close friend, talking excitedly and without pause. I knew I was on the right track with the changes I was making, because I kept producing beautiful symbolic dreams. This friend has a library of Gnostic works from the mystical traditions, and he found all the images in my dreams in his books, sometimes illustrated by engravings. They featured archetypal themes. For months I dreamed fertile dreams of making love underwater, or of sleeping in a forest bed made of mosses and ferns.

The energy released by the remedy and expressed in these healing themes pushed me to make the radical changes I needed to make in order to create new openings in my life. I finished the unsatisfying relationship I was in by asking my partner to move out, and I went on to travel to Egypt, a place that was to have a profound impact on me and where I grew a great deal spiritually.

On another trip, my dreams alerted me that I was on the wrong track. On arriving at a Sufi spiritual centre in Turkey, which I was shocked to find now debased as a tourist attraction, I dreamed that I looked down at my right hand and saw that all the precious jewels had been torn from the ring I always wear, and that the gold was twisted and torn as a result of their forcible removal.

Tremendous energy is released in me when I follow these messages from the unconscious and go with the direction in which it flows. When I ignore them, I feel unmotivated and fall into a succession of exhausting, sleepless nights where there are no dreams to show me the way.

Alan has vivid dreams of wild animals pursuing him night after night. Although they are exhausting dreams, he feels better for having them because he believes that they express his deep feelings of rage and frustration; emotions that he is not normally aware of in his waking moments. When he goes through periods of time in which he does not recall his dreams, he feels more loaded with negative emotions, which tends to make him feel prickly and resentful in interactions with other people.

Different Responses to Homeopathic Remedies

The way I work is usually to give a patient occasional single doses of the appropriate remedy, monitoring the changes that it brings about over a period of time so that we can share insights about what is happening. This is known as the classical approach. When one remedy is given at a time, its energetic effects are given enough time to unfold throughout all levels of the person: body, mind, and soul. I use the same technique I use initially to diagnose a remedy by observing the patterns of the soul: I observe the movement of the remedy as it acts on the energy body of the person.

It can take several weeks or months to evaluate the action of each dose of a remedy. Each person's pace of response and progress are different, so each person's treatment takes a different length of time and follows a unique course. Sometimes the response appears impressive and instantaneous, and at other times it can seem more erratic, or even imperceptible until we look back together with hindsight. Timing is often of key importance in determining what use a person can make of a remedy, as well as the resources currently available in his or her life.

The energy of the homeopathic remedy will stimulate the individual in such a way as to help him or her find a solution. I cannot always predict the ways in which a person's soul will solve any problems needing to be dealt with. Sometimes it is only after months or even years of observation that I am able to identify the pattern of healing that the remedy has unfolded in a particular individual. Sometimes the solution arrived at does not at first seem to be the best possible outcome; however, as the healing unfolds on a deeper level, perhaps over some time, the intelligence of the ways of the soul becomes more apparent.

The different expectations that people bring to a homeopathic consultation can also affect the outcome of the remedy. While some will use the energy offered by the homeopathic remedy to transform their lives, others will refuse to see anything more in homeopathy than a mundane medical process aimed only at the relief of symptoms. These people prefer to take a different remedy for every new ailment, with the result that homeopathic remedies improve their physical symptoms without them ever finding a deeper cure.

Part of the difference in how people respond to homeopathy lies in where an individual is on his or her soul journey, but an equal part of it lies in the homeopath's ability to be a true healer, to tune in to and perceive what is needed to clear the blocks to the free flow of soul energy in each person.

The Contrast with Conventional Medicine

Conventional medicine is mistakenly built on the notion that you can get rid of a disease as if it is somehow not part of the person who is 'dis-eased'. However, there is usually no single cause for an illness. All illness has spiritual, emotional, physical and environmental determinants and aspects. In particular it is shaped by the ways in which you handle a multitude of different experiences and stimuli. In order really to heal yourself, you have to pay attention to all these aspects of your being.

The longer I have practised, the more I have been bemused by the power claimed by medics and vested in orthodox medicine by the general population. In some respects it is a surprisingly unsophisticated system. Diagnoses are really labels for a group of symptoms, and the range of treatments available is rather limited. Yet we expect medicine to save us from the inevitability of death. I think it is in part due to our fear of death that we give so much power to doctors in our society. We are afraid of dying, especially if we feel we have not done what we really want to do in our lives. This is the lesson I learned from the cancer patients whom Laurence Le Shan described. They were able to affect the outcome of their apparently terminal diagnoses by seizing hold of life with both hands.

Lianne found that homeopathy allowed her to let go of a crippling fear of death which made her overanxious about even trivial symptoms. She had experienced enormous difficulties with the medical profession before she started homeopathic treatment, as a result of having been hospitalized with asthma frequently as a child. She told me, 'When I came to homeopathy I had a very bad relationship with the medical profession – I was fearful and intimidated by doctors, and very anxious about my health. I lost my faith that it was possible to heal myself, and I regained it through your confidence that homeopathic treatment could help me. Using homeopathy has meant I have achieved a level of health I no longer thought was possible, and it has allowed me to have so many more choices in my lifestyle.'

Lianne found that homeopathy succeeded where conventional medicine failed, partially because the treatment substantially improved her asthma and other ailments, and in part because of the relationship she was able to forge with me as her homeopath. 'My relationship with my homeopathic practitioner is very important to me, and I feel cared for as a whole person. My homeopath has always had an immediate ability to focus in on me and what's happening with me, even when I telephone. She's never been too pushy with me when I've needed to come to realizations in my own time. She's clear and consistent in dealing with me, and open about sharing her homeopathic knowledge. When I came to her over a decade ago, I needed the opportunity to discover more about myself, and what homeopathy meant for me. I feel we share an understanding of the mystery of life, and homeopathy has opened my mind to energy. There's something magical about homeopathy, because it's a process that can never really be defined. It has been profoundly important in my life.'

Lianne's homeopathic treatment allowed her to find her own way of experiencing the spiritual, and by doing this she came to terms with her fear of death. 'I need to feel connected to something bigger than myself, and I've taken to going outside and star-gazing. The sense that the spiritual and the political can co-exist is very important to me, and helps me to deal with the fears that used to paralyse me about death.'

Choosing Whether or Not to Take a Homeopathic Remedy

Homeopathy is about self-healing. When someone takes a homeopathic remedy, it is his or her own energy body that does the work rather than a drug imposing chemical changes on the body's biochemistry. A homeopathic remedy works by giving the energy body an opportunity to reharmonize and heal itself. This means that the progress towards self-healing follows its own pace and unfolds according to the unique situation and history of each individual. Just as the remedy is not directly responsible for the changes that a person's energy body brings about in itself, so I am not directly responsible for the effects of the remedy. It is the soul that is in charge of the healing process. I believe that the soul has its own intelligence, and I know that we cannot always understand its intelligence.

When I was teaching homeopathy in Beirut to a mixed class of Sufis, doctors and housewives, we had a fruitful discussion about the ethics of whether or not it was appropriate for someone to take a particular remedy. The woman in question who had come to the clinic for treatment was a devout Muslim who spent many hours a day in prayer, reaching states of exquisite ecstasy. Behind Samia's devotion was an arid personal life in which she felt totally unappreciated by her domineering and self-centred husband. The hours Samia spent in prayer were also hours when she turned her back on the world and lost herself in a transcendent realm. They did not help her to alter her mundane existence. The question we debated was whether the remedy indicated for her might reduce these blissful states and make her feel more miserable as a first step in dealing with the reality of the situation in which she was living. My own argument was that if the deeper needs of the soul were for her to lose some of her ability to attain religious ecstasy, then that would be exactly what would happen under the influence of the remedy.

If the states of spiritual ecstasy were genuinely grounded in her soul, and were not a form of escapism, then I doubted they would disappear.

From my experience, I believed that, were this woman to lose some of her ecstatic experience, it would be compensated by an integration of her whole life, so that she would also experience less despair, for the intensity of her religious ecstasy was matched by the depth of her despair when struggling to communicate with her husband or to have any sort of satisfactory family life. The changes that homeopathy brings about are not predictable, because they depend on the complexities of each person's situation. The expectations I have of how a particular remedy will work are based on my experience of how that remedy has worked for other people, which may not always be relevant in someone else's case.

After this discussion, I left the decision as to whether to take the remedy or not up to her. She chose not to take it. I was mindful that it may have been the soul's wisdom for her not to do so; the reason was not for me to know. There is a higher intelligence at work than our intellectual or even our intuitive understanding of a given situation. This higher intelligence emanates from our soul, and it may determine what each person needs in order to move along on their path to healing.

chapter 2

*the journey
towards cure*

There are many different routes which people follow between taking a homeopathic remedy and becoming well. In this section I shall explore the range of journeys different people make on their way towards cure.

Some people's response to taking a homeopathic remedy can be dramatic. They experience an immediate transformation in their energy pattern, which creates a mood of elation and euphoria as their energy is charged up by the remedy. These people may find that their physical symptoms are cured very quickly. Even when the transformation is not so instantaneous, most people describe a greater sense of well-being, a stronger vitality, more peace or contentment and more energy after taking a homeopathic remedy.

Josie came to see me at the end of a long winter during which she suffered one viral infection after another. She had developed a chronic sore throat and a problem with catarrh, which meant she needed to clear her throat every few minutes when speaking. Her energy was very low and she was also feeling very depressed because of her long-term relationship with a man who was unaffectionate and self-sufficient in a way that she felt excluded her. He came in late from work only to sleep, and went out fishing or hiking every weekend. Josie blamed herself and felt she was neither interesting nor successful, unlike her partner. Because of the lack of confidence that stopped her from expressing her emotional needs in the relationship, I gave her a single dose of the homeopathic remedy Baryta carbonicum.

On her next visit two weeks later, Josie told me that she had felt better instantly. 'I was really impressed that the frog in my throat cleared up straight-away and the depression I had been suffering lifted. I feel much stronger and more confident. I came for homeopathy at just the right time because now there's a big crisis at work and my job is on the line. I realize that my work is very important to me because it's what I believe in, and even if I end up unemployed for a period of time that doesn't mean I'm a burden on my partner.' Josie's remedy couldn't change her partner's behaviour, but she had gained sufficient self-confidence to realize that the decision was completely up to her whether she wanted to persevere with this relationship. By feeling much better about her own strengths, she was more able to work on changing the dynamic of their interaction.

Homeopathic remedies work by focusing the soul's own self-healing on the specific areas where energy is stagnated. You can contribute to the healing process by having a clear intention of what you want to achieve; this enables you to channel the energy released by the action of the remedy towards blocked areas. The more ready you are to utilize this energy, the better results you will have in healing yourself.

Where you are unable to do this by yourself, the appropriate remedy will enable you to do what is needed; raising your energy levels so you can respond to your circumstances in new ways, 'seizing the moment' to make the most of opportunities that come your way. As a result of this increased energy you can face making changes, following them through and accepting the consequences of any ensuing upheaval in your life.

The curative action of the correct remedy mediates your perception of the situation you find yourself in, clarifying your relationship to your circumstances. You no longer feel like a victim, because you see the opportunities for change or growth which you were blind to when feeling stuck. The remedy opens up a feeling of internal spaciousness, which is the space of possibilities. Even in a seemingly hopeless situation, the right remedy seems to enable you to make more sense of things, opening a window for new choices in the way you respond to challenges.

Janet reported that, 'One of the profound ways I've seen homeopathic remedies affect me is in breaking my obsessional thinking. I tend to get anxious and obsessive about things, thinking they must be done in a certain way. Homeopathy often surprised me. After taking a dose of my constitutional remedy my mood would lift, allowing me to see things in a different way. Often it would surprise me, the way I could suddenly see a different spin on things, or the way something else would suddenly improve.

'When I'm very stressed and anxious I tend to get tunnel vision, but each time I took a remedy, it would calm me down, stop me being rigid and enable me to look at different options.'

Some people only realize how radically their perceptions have been altered by a homeopathic remedy when they are confronted by a dramatic situation which puts their attitudes to the test. Through such experiences we learn that each situation can either be traumatic or a chance to heal ourselves. It is up to us to use the potential that a difficult situation offers us for healing whatever we find so difficult. The role of the homeopathic remedy is to enable us to open up to a range of possible responses in situations that we previously considered non-negotiable.

Heather, an artist aged 45, had always been tormented by a fear of death, which would overwhelm her every time she was about to finish a major painting. We had discussed this during treatment, and I'd prescribed the homeopathic remedy Arsenicum album (see page 175), because of her existential terror combined with a range of other health problems. After the remedy, Heather's cat allergy cleared up, her digestive symptoms disappeared, her arthritis improved and she felt much more confident and productive. It was only when she was confronted with an unexpected drama that Heather realized she no longer feared death. One day when out walking, she was called into a house by a distraught young girl whose mother had collapsed. Heather called an ambulance and stayed with the girl, watching the mother die. Instead of exacerbating her own fears of death, Heather discovered that after this experience she was no longer afraid. 'I would have expected it to really bother me, seeing how someone can be suddenly struck down, and those around are helpless to save them. Instead, I feel more philosophical. Worrying about it can't change what might happen to me at any moment.'

Homeopathic remedies make you more conscious of how the situation you are living in contributes to your distorted energy pattern. For some people, therefore, taking a remedy can have profound effects on their day-to-day circumstances. It mobilizes the energy within necessary to make difficult but necessary adjustments in their lives. They may decide they need to change their job or let go of a relationship. The effects of a remedy may unsettle their long-standing friendships as they become more confident to say what they think and feel.

Shortly after starting homeopathic treatment for endometriosis, a gynaecological disorder in which patches of uterine lining migrate to other abdominal organs, Denise unexpectedly fell in love, even though she had been living happily with her partner for some years. She was reluctant to break her existing relationship up when her head told her that there was really nothing wrong. In spite of her feelings of guilt, her heart pushed her to leave her partner and give the new relationship a chance. It was only once she had moved in with the second man that she discovered the vast improvement that living with this more compatible partner made to her life.

Since the soul has its own wisdom, the outcome of treatment is not always predictable. The solutions brought about after taking remedies are often creative. You need to keep an open mind to what may unfold, rather than having expectations about what should or should not happen, because your future might turn out to be something completely other than what you had in mind.

Miles had been plagued by doubt and intense dissatisfaction with his friendships from early adolescence onwards, which seemed to account for his chronic migraine headaches. It was only after taking his homeopathic remedy, Thuja, that he realized that he was uncertain about his sexual orientation and identity. Once he had become aware of what it was that was really troubling him, he was able to start thinking about these issues and, with the help of his remedy, he became much happier, even though it took him years to come to terms fully with his homosexuality.

Sometimes this process of clarification, where the remedy reveals to a person the fundamental issues that need dealing with, can be long, slow and painful. It unfolds through a peeling away of defensive attitudes to reveal what those core problems are. As this growth process progresses, the person becomes painfully aware of the restrictions they have been living with. They may initially be more distressed as a result of realizing how distant they feel from their soul's journey. They are forced to start taking responsibility for themselves and making the choices necessary in order to get themselves back on track.

After decades of teaching, Anne could not cope with the increased bureaucracy at school, coupled with the stress of state inspections and a head at the helm who did not inspire confidence. She found herself unable to go in to work because of her exhaustion, and took an extended period of time off. The first few months were just spent recovering from burnout (see page 85), which I treated with the homeopathic remedy Cocculus.

Anne surprised herself when she realized that she had already made the decision that she was not going back. Although she did not have a firm idea about another occupation, Anne applied for early retirement on health grounds. Stopping work signalled the start of a protracted period of processing burried emotions. When she had been teaching, fears and anxieties had plagued her at night, causing insomnia, anxious dreams and feelings of foreboding about vague disasters that she could not put her finger on. These emotions returned, and Anne became aware of the deep feelings of depression, loneliness and sadness that the years of constant working had masked. Her energy remained low throughout this period, stopping her from throwing herself into a series of distractions.

After these core issues had emerged and formed a clear picture of her underlying state, Anne responded well to the remedy Calcarea carbonica (see page 184), which I gave her because she seemed to lack both the energy and confidence to deal with the challenges in her life. The remedy enabled her to allocate her energetic resources more efficiently and just concentrate on essentials. She gave herself just one little goal a day, allowing herself time to immerse herself in all her difficult feelings. At first, more than the company of friends, Anne needed to feel that her life was congruent with her spiritual nature. She was undergoing a protracted re-evaluation of her life, in which she saw clearly how the lifestyle she had created had not nourished her soul. Anne was sensitive emotionally and spiritually, and became clear that her soul's purpose was to work on her over-critical mind in order to allow love to flourish.

Anne had a lot of anger about the exploitative ways that so-called 'spiritual teachers' had treated her in the past during her spiritual search, abusing her trust, and a lot of frustration about religious authorities and dogmas that prevented her from exploring a loving relationship with someone who had joined a spiritual community. This relationship represented the limits of what could change, because he had taken a decision to stick to the outward forms of his religious path, including celibacy. This meant she had to turn inside herself to look for emotional strength to deal with this deep disappointment. She could neither react as if it were a rejection of her nor reject him, for she felt deeply connected to him. Her lesson was to learn to develop and rely on her own internal resources, no longer looking for external structure or validation, nor relying on institutionalized religious guidance. She joined a group of peers exploring their own inner journey, who encouraged each other in finding their own forms of spirituality.

There are some people who experience the positive benefits caused by their homeopathic remedy but who resist making the changes necessary for healing to be complete. By resisting such changes, they may miss out on some of the healing effects of the remedy. The right remedy revitalizes your energy body, cleansing, restoring and stimulating it to provide the necessary energy for appropriate changes. But some people find it easier to stay with what is familiar rather than to risk failing. Sometimes they feel that they do not know how to make the changes.

Sometimes they try to ignore, deny or repress the problem that their homeopathic remedy has made them conscious of.

Simon, an alcoholic, responded very well to the homeopathic remedy China officinalis but was unable to stop drinking and allow his system to clear enough for the remedy to take hold at a more profound level. He refused to see a counsellor or do anything to examine the reasons for his drinking. Admitting that he was an alcoholic would have been the first step towards doing something about it, but he preferred to hide behind a façade of arrogant intellectualism, despite the fact that years of heavy drink had reduced his mental and physical powers. He felt critical and superior towards other people, even though he lived alone, could not hold down a job and was not doing well as a parent. He was afraid of intimacy, and he described all his sexual encounters since breaking up with his wife as 'sordid'. The dark side of his sexuality was expressed in violent sexual dreams, but he was reluctant to discuss them with anyone. Although the remedy released a lot of energy and improved the physical symptoms of Simon's alcoholism quite dramatically – showing that homeopathy could be of great help in his process of recovery – he chose to discontinue treatment and carry on drinking.

Homeopaths have observed that profound healing progresses from the soul level through the psychological level and then to the physical level.

Healing progresses from the inside outwards, as the body seeks to externalize disease.

Healing progresses from more important organs to less important ones.

Healing progresses from the top of the body downwards.

Symptoms get better in reverse order – that is, the latest symptom first, followed by more long-standing problems.

The Healing Crisis

Some people find that after taking a homeopathic remedy they suffer a temporary worsening of some of their ailments. Homeopaths call this worsening an 'aggravation', but in fact this is usually a sign of a healing crisis in which a patient temporarily feels worse before he or she gets better. People usually describe a greater sense of general well-being and optimism, despite the fact that superficial symptoms may be worse for a short time. They also manage to deal with physical symptoms in a better way than usual. Their symptoms seem to be less burdensome, even when they may be more painful.

Janice went through an unusually intense aggravation of her allergic eczema after a dose of Medorrhinum (see page 203). It produced even more inflammation than ever before, and tremendous itchiness which prevented her from sleeping at night for some weeks. Overnight her skin would flake off and the sheets were often blood-stained in the morning where she had broken the skin with her scratching. Because the eczema had been a lifelong illness for her, this aggravation made her feel hopeful that her condition was being affected at a deep level. 'This faith sustained me through the bad flare-up of my eczema, in which my skin kept literally scaling off. After six weeks I came out with near-perfect skin. Now I think of it like a butterfly coming out of a chrysalis.'

When people suffer from an aggravation of some of their symptoms during a healing crisis, it may be a result of toxicity coming out of their system. It may be a transient reaction as the remedy starts to take effect. Alternatively, it may be due to their energy being redistributed in a new pattern. The change in their energy pattern causes a corresponding alteration in their symptoms. Some symptoms feel more intense because energy is building up like a dam behind the blockages that cause those symptoms. Eventually the energy will push through the obstruction. Some symptoms are relieved immediately as the energy blockages that caused them are released.

The homeopathic law of cure states that more fundamental problems respond to treatment before the less fundamental ones. Your energy always improves first, then your psychological state, followed by an improvement in your physical symptoms. The fact that the remedy improves their energy first explains why people feel better in themselves when they take a homeopathic remedy even though some of their physical symptoms initially get worse.

Veronica, who was suffering from repeated kidney infections, had been told that it was inevitable that she would keep having them, because the lining of her kidneys was covered with scarring from previous infections. Feeling ill and depleted after endless courses of antibiotics, she described how her kidney infections had started years previously during a particularly stressful working situation in which she had used alcohol to wind down in the evenings. After a dose of the remedy Berberis, she immediately felt a surge of energy, but the kidney pains felt worse. In spite of the physical pain she was in shortly after taking each of the first three doses of the remedy, Veronica was convinced that the remedy was working well because she felt so much more positive. She was only aware how much the gusto with which she normally lived her life had been reduced once she got back to her old self. The remedy produced a discharge for a few weeks, and her physical discomfort quickly cleared. She has not had another infection for years.

Sometimes a homeopathic remedy causes the aggravation of psychological rather than physical symptoms. Although intense feelings often come out after a remedy, I have never seen them overwhelm a person or be too much to handle. They are feelings that have been present all along under the surface but have not been allowed into conscious awareness. They may have been suppressed because the person is afraid of the intensity of these feelings, or perhaps because of a fear of the changes he or she will have to make if these feelings are acknowledged.

Shelley was horrified by the strength of her sudden upsurge of murderous feelings towards her husband after taking a dose of her remedy, Nitric acidum. They seemed to arise from resentment at her own dependency on him. Shelley responded by consulting a psychotherapist and embarked on a lengthy process of re-evaluating the relationship, in which she was gradually able to moderate her demanding behaviour and start to look at other ways to meet her emotional needs. She was then able to accept the positive qualities in the relationship, and the time she spent with her husband was no longer soured by her feeling of unmet needs.

Remedies work by releasing negative energy patterns. Sometimes people panic when they are no longer aware of the knotted place inside which has been taking up so much energy. Once the energy is flowing freely, they may interpret the resulting spaciousness as a sign of a gaping emptiness inside. If we have lived many years in a stuck pattern, we may feel like newborn babies struggling to learn how to experience things. We can learn from their innocent wonder by trying to enjoy the process of finding out how to manifest this new sense of well-being rather than being in a hurry to put something else in the place of the void. It's important to allow time for something to emerge rather than being frightened of change.

Other people become aware of a different sort of emptiness within them after taking a remedy. This is the void which was already there but which they were not aware of. The action of the remedy helps them find new ways to fill it.

Jeff experienced a void after taking the remedy Sulphur (see page 237). He realized that he habitually filled himself up on high-calorie foods with little nutritional content, and that when he did not eat much he felt ravenously hungry. He decided to amplify this craving by eating nothing but fruit for several weeks. After the cravings for food subsided some weeks later, he suffered a terrible gnawing in the pit of his stomach which became more and more intense. This sensation was very different to hunger, although it had been driving him to eat in a misguided attempt to fill it. He realized that very early on in his life the act of eating had become associated with unmet spiritual needs rather than the requirements of his body for fuel. The craving for calorific foods emphasized his need for other forms of sustenance. Like other addicts, he had tried to fill the void within himself with a substance that was a substitute for love. But as is the way with addiction, Jeff had become more and more unhappy and increasingly dependent on increasing amounts of this substance.

Jeff was able to tolerate the discomfort of fasting, and just carried right on with the same strategy of eating very little. Eventually he became more satisfied on his fruit diet and a new pattern emerged that was related to his need for food rather than his spiritual hunger. He then added other healthy foods until he had a well-balanced diet.

Jeff also embarked on a deeper journey of self-discovery in which he explored aspects of himself which he had denied for decades. That journey was to involve exploring his sexuality, learning how to develop intimacy and using meditation and other spiritual practices to deepen his sense of connection with others and the world.

Sometimes people find that, although their remedy cures the problem they were concerned about straightaway, a new symptom arises which they had not had before. When this happens, it is a sign that they need to make more changes in their lives. Only when a person has made these fundamental changes can the symptom be cured.

Frank came to see me about his lack of confidence at work. This problem responded well to the remedy Argentum nitricum, but an itchy eruption came out on his chest which wept fluid and crusted over. It became apparent that he had a deeper confidence issue, in the arena of his sexual relationships. Whenever he was in a relationship for any length of time, he became impotent. He interpreted the problem as a sign of boredom, but in fact it was connected with his fears of intimacy. The sexual dysfunction had stopped him from persevering with any relationship, because he found he functioned better with casual sex. The skin problem remained until he cleared up his fundamental fear of closeness, which took some time.

part 2

preparing for soul work

chapter 3

making a start

There are a number of ways you can cleanse your energy body before you start the soul work of homeopathic therapy:

✥ You can facilitate the process of homeopathy by clearing out any obvious toxins. Stop taking stimulants like coffee, tea, tobacco as well as any stronger drugs.

✥ Don't use recreational drugs and, wherever possible, avoid conventional medications (although talk to your doctor before stopping any medication you are receiving). You need to be cautious about taking any drugs, because all medications have negative as well as positive effects on health, so always check with your homeopath beforehand. Conventional medicines work in an antagonistic way to homeopathy: they are aimed at palliating specific physical symptoms rather than rebalancing the energy imbalance that lies behind them. Treatments such as steroids or antibiotics blight a person's energy body, compromising its ability to heal and become well. The use of toxic drugs often contributes to grafting yet more layers of trauma onto the energy body, which may have to be cleared by homeopathy before deeper healing can begin.

🌀 The liver was considered the seat of the will by ancient physicians. Your will is the driving force behind manifesting your intent in the world. Cleansing the liver helps to restimulate your drive to discover your own unique goal. Many people find that following a fat-free, liver-cleansing diet for a period of weeks is one factor in helping them to develop the willpower to go on and deal with addictions.

🌀 Paying attention to fundamental aspects of your lifestyle such as like diet and exercise is an important way to nurture the bodily vehicle of your soul. Cut out any junk food and drink plenty of pure water. By eating fresh, organic wholefoods, you can minimize the level of chemical toxins you ingest in your diet. Regular physical activity, whether in the form of exercise, yoga, dancing or walking, will help to keep your body functioning well. Exercise usually improves your physical energy.

You can also make a number of lifestyle changes which may help your energy body:

🌀 In working with the energy body it is important to pay attention to your levels of energy. Unless you have a slow metabolism, pushing your body is not the answer to low energy; instead, you need to ease up on yourself, rest more and let yourself just be, rather than ceaselessly making yourself do. You will then have more of an idea of your real energy levels.

🌀 For the benefit of your soul it is important to create some mental space through simple forms of meditation, whether that means just sitting quietly for half an hour every day, being in nature more, or following a more structured sort of meditation practice.

🌀 You need to pay attention to the kinds of people you spend time with, and to consider whether they are draining or inspiring you. You also need to think about the activities you are filling your days with, and ask yourself whether they are augmenting or diminishing your energy levels.

Once you have taken a homeopathic remedy there are a number of things which you can do to contribute to your own self-healing:

❧ Once the remedy stimulates your energy, it is important to sustain that sense of well-being rather than using it up by expending yourself in a lot of frenetic, unfocused activity.

❧ Remedies will help you to achieve and maintain the necessary changes in your energy body, but formulating your own intentions as to what needs to be transformed in your life is also important. Being active rather than passive in the process facilitates the changes your energy body will make once you are no longer blocking it.

❧ The effects of a remedy can sometimes be quite drastic. You need to ensure that the dosage and repetition of remedies are monitored carefully, so that you are not taking more of a remedy than you actually need. Your homeopath will help you evaluate how much or how little is best for you.

Max's case is one example of how paying attention to these simple guidelines helps you take responsibility for your own health care. He says, 'I had to change some basic habits in my lifestyle – I stopped smoking just before starting homeopathy, and gave up all the coffee and stimulants I'd been using to boost my energy levels. Once homeopathic treatment raised my level of health I began to see that I am capable of improving my own health. I do not always expect little white pills to take everything away. I'm no longer fearful about doctors and I don't allow myself to be patronized. I've realized the limits of any specialist's knowledge and I've learned to look after myself.'

In the next two chapters I shall explain in detail two tools which you can use to prepare yourself for the soul work of homeopathic treatment. These approaches will help you to start the process of finding out more about the patterns of your energy body and where your energy may be unbalanced or stuck. In Chapter 4 I explore how you can identify your soul's unique spiritual path. In Chapter 5 I discuss how you can discover the core theme or themes which lie at the heart of your emotional and physical problems. In Chapter 6 I shall demonstrate how homeopathy understands and treats each of the psychological problems that constitute the core themes of different peoples' souls.

chapter 4

*different paths
of the soul*

Finding Your Path in Life

We all have our own personal spiritual path through life, the way of engaging with life which infuses our lives with meaning. You can tell when you are on the correct path, even if you cannot articulate exactly what it is. When you are on the right path, you feel a sense of congruence about your pursuits, and you notice that you spend more time doing things that energize you. A simple test to indicate whether you are on the right path for you is to ask yourself how much of the day you spend doing things you really enjoy or feel moved by and how much doing things that make you feel negative in some way.

When you are doing what you want to do because it is in tune with your deeper self, you are not acting out of guilt, obligation or need. You are doing something because it is a natural expression of who you are at a fundamental level. It is what gives your life a sense of meaning and, perhaps, a mission.

Feeling sure of your purpose means you automatically affect those around you. We all know people we consider as wise or good-hearted, people who will listen to others, who are always doing things for others and who do not seem to need to talk very much about themselves and what they are doing. These are people who are actively engaged in life, with an optimistic approach to the situations they encounter. They seem to have found and be following their personal map. We can feel their intelligent awareness and their lively spirits, and they provide role models for the rest of us. Energy flows naturally through these people, enabling them to keep giving to others; they do not need to hold on to it or claim it as their own personal property.

We all get stuck sometimes as we travel along our journeys in life. When this happens it is because our energy has become blocked in some way. We are all familiar with the idea of writer's block, a state of psychological paralysis that prevents creative inspiration from getting through. We all have blocks like this which prevent our energy from flowing freely so that we may have difficulty actualizing our intentions.

One way of finding out whether you are on the path that resonates with your soul's desires is to discover whether there are any such blockages obstructing the free flow of your energy. Blocks are usually obvious because they paralyse us in almost every waking moment of the day. As you look at how you are going about your daily activities, you can see the result of this disturbed energy pattern.

The blocks we discover within our lives usually fall into the pattern of a homeopathic remedy. This remedy will be the appropriate one to help you realign yourself to your own unique path.

Crisis or Quest

Our journey through life is a quest for meaning. We search for meaning in our relationships, in our work and in every aspect of our lives, and it is this search that pushes many of us into a deeper awareness of our personal spiritual path. Each spiritual path has both positive and negative qualities. When you lose perspective about the things you are involved with, you may get polarized into some of its negative aspects. This can happen when you feel frustrated or disillusioned about things that have been important to you. At this point you may be experiencing a crisis in your search for personal meaning.

Crisis can be precipitated by unexpected loss or change in your life, such as when your partner leaves, you have a miscarriage, you are fired, you have to move house, you break a leg, or even if a beloved pet dies. Such events can destabilize us, throwing up distressing responses that bring us to question the purpose of life. Whether we respond to these events as a crisis or as a new stage of our quest depends on our internal resources.

It is scary to fall ill or lose something important. You want to hang on to the sense of identity that you have so painstakingly built, whether through your job, your relationship or your perception of yourself as healthy and independent. But when these crises occur you discover you are not so healthy, whole or independent. You discover or rediscover your neediness or feelings of failure, inadequacy and fearfulness.

In acknowledging these feelings, you have the opportunity to find new ways of approaching life and developing your interests. You can deal with upsetting feelings by facing your problems, growing through the painful experience and becoming more whole as a result. Because of this, you may find later (once you have recovered from the crisis) that you are grateful for having been shaken out of your complacency.

Illness is often an unsettling event that forces change on you. Whether you are laid up with glandular fever, off work with repetitive strain injury or struck down by a heart attack, you need to rediscover more whole ways of living your life.

Shirley literally nearly died of a broken heart when her long-term relationship broke down. She suffered a severe heart attack. I gave her the homeopathic remedy Bryonia when she developed a severe chest infection while she was still weak after her attack, which meant she sat propped up at night coughing for hours. As well as clearing up the virus, this remedy got her out of bed during the day for the first time in months and kick-started her life again. It cleared up the chronic breathlessness of heart failure and the fatigue left in the wake of her heart attack, and gave her the energy to start expressing her creativity. She decided to give herself a new lease of life by going to art school and regained her joyful optimistic attitude.

In some ways the cataclysmic events which constitute crises in your spiritual quest can be easier to deal with than situations where you find your life stuck in a dead-end street, because the dramatic nature of the circumstances forces you to respond. Situations of chronic stagnation may take a long time to recognize, and even then you may feel that things have been going on for so long that there is no urgency for change. This state of inertia means that many people do not make adjustments until forced into them by apparently external events.

The Archetypal Paths

There is no single path of the soul which everyone should follow. The mystical traditions of diverse religions such as Sufism, Hinduism, Christianity and Buddhism have mapped out a number of common paths. Each one may broadly suit certain individuals, but there is no single way that applies to everyone. In fact, each of our journeys is as unique as we are. How then can we find guidance along the way?

In the remainder of this chapter I shall describe the nine archetypal paths I have observed. These are the paths of action, experience, homemaking, love, reparation, service, social activism, transcendence and wisdom. Exploring the values embodied in each of these well-trodden paths can help you to define what attracts your soul. This may well be a combination of elements from more than one of the archetypal paths.

For each of the paths I have given a general impression of what it involves and a list of the positive and negative qualities associated with people who follow that path, gleaned from my knowledge of the range of homeopathic remedies patients have required to help them on their journeys.

For each path I have also included an archetypal remedy. This is one of the remedies whose energy pattern most closely resonates to the energy pattern of people on this path. There are a number of other remedies which may be more appropriate for you personally, but the one I have selected will give you a good idea of what can happen if you get stuck while pursuing a particular course in life. You can then turn to the entry for the remedy in Part 3 and see if the profile gives you more insight into your own energy pattern on a psychological and spiritual level. This helps you to see your own strengths and weaknesses more clearly. It also helps you to see how getting stuck on your path might affect the ways you relate to other people, your behaviour and your personality. When we feel obstructed on our path, we start to display the negative qualities associated with that path. The remedy corresponding to our core issues frees us to move on along our path and allows us to access its positive qualities instead.

To decide which path or paths come closest to describing your journey, think about what motivates you at a deeper level and what your soul's goals are. Try to decide what your fundamental drives are in life. Ask yourself whether you feel your deepest desires are frustrated. Discover what needs healing in yourself so that you can live your life to the full. When you find out what needs healing, you will be closer to finding your own path. Homeopathy helps you to connect to your soul, and when you connect to your soul, you find out that you are already on your way.

The Path of Action

The task of people affiliated with the path of action is to manifest spiritual truths in the world, bringing a consciousness of the realm of the soul to organized activities. Their aim is to bring conscious awareness to the way things are run, the way we create things, make things and build things. When these activities are undertaken by someone living in accordance with this spiritual path, they can be imbued with a sense of harmony and carried out according to methods that respect and follow natural laws. For instance, teachers who are on this path succeed in conveying the underlying natural laws behind their discipline. In the field of architecture, those on this path use harmonious principles such as those vested in sacred geometry. Those who practise homeopathy use principles founded on observing the laws of nature and the natural processes of self-healing.

People on the path of action usually have a discerning mind and an ability to penetrate behind the world of appearances into the heart of things. They develop an astute ability to observe. Qualities such as sustained motivation, high creative drive, clarity, care, conscientious attention to detail and an orderly way of going about things are important for those on this path.

People on this path may need to clarify their attitudes to power, so that their personal power is not used in a controlling way but is allowed to manifest itself through the innate strength of what they are creating. They need to acknowledge power as an impersonal attribute of the realm of the soul rather than belonging to the egotistical realm of the personality. They may need to learn humility as well as to have courage.

POSITIVE QUALITIES ASSOCIATED WITH THOSE ON THE PATH OF ACTION

- People on this path are proactive and effective in achieving goals. They are intense, go-getting, dynamic and vigorous. They tend to be influential; they are movers and shakers.
- They can be enthusiastic entrepreneurs with a sense of initiative. They are practical and successful, resourceful and industrious.
- They are ingenious, quick-thinking, incisive and goal-oriented. They can catalyse situations and move them on effectively. In a team situation they can be instrumental in actualizing goals. They have a keen awareness about processes and obstacles in their professional arena.

- They are often workaholics and can become overidentified with their goals.
- They can make insufficient time to spend with loved ones, as a result of being consumed by their projects or work.
- They can be cut off from their emotional side.
- They can behave in a manner that is intrusive, aggressive and pushy.
- They are over-critical. They can be harsh or sarcastic in dealing with others, especially those who they feel are less able. They see themselves as unable to 'suffer fools gladly'.
- They can be hard-headed and unable to make allowances for other people's needs, which they interpret as weaknesses.
- They may be controlling and perfectionist. They are often unable to delegate.
- They may become officious and fanatical.

Archetypal Remedy

These qualities belong archetypally to the remedy Nux vomica. See the remedy profile on page 211 for the picture that may emerge when energy gets blocked in those on this path.

The Path of Experience

This can be a path of ecstatic being. The key element that attracts individuals to this path is the search for intensity of experience. People who pursue intensity can appear to others to have a childlike quality of enthusiasm and wonder. This is a result of being completely immersed in the moment, rather than being caught up in thoughts and feelings about past or present scenarios. They do not seem overly serious about life and do not defer the business of living till some later date once they have got their obligations out of the way. Their attitude is that 'life is for living,' and they allow themselves pleasure in fulfilling their purpose.

People on this path do not necessarily see themselves as on a spiritual journey, because they are so immersed in the immediacy of their lived experience. What is important for them is being in the here and now. They may even be attracted to profane pursuits and find themselves attempting to imbue them with a sense of the sacred through the intensity of their engagement with them.

The challenge for those on this path is to learn that all experiences are a manifestation of pure energy. They need to become less attached to whether any particular experience feels good or not and just accept it either way. Instead of trying to make things feel good or exciting all the time, they must learn to enter into whatever experiences life offers with the same intensity.

This path is about increasing awareness of the possibilities inherent in all experience, and living life charged up as if you are in a high-energy field. People on this path do not have to deaden the intensity of their responses because things feel too overwhelming. Neither do they need to create intense experiences artificially. People who are aligned with this path often have the ability to make the everyday sacred.

POSITIVE QUALITIES ASSOCIATED WITH THOSE ON THE PATH OF EXPERIENCE

- People on this path often feel a fresh sense of innocence. They have an open curiosity and a keen sense of spontaneity.
- If they expand their awareness, they can access states of contemplation, reflection, awe and wonder.
- They feel responsive and connected to others.
- They feel inspired.
- They may be impulsive, intense, emotional and effusive.
- They feel sensitive, sensual, responsive and soulful.
- They behave in ways that are spirited, fiery, energetic and passionate.
- They move easily into states of elation and rapture, and can achieve ecstatic states of bliss.

- They experience a need to bring drama into their lives in order to create a sense of intensity rather than going more deeply into everyday experience. They risk exploding whatever situation they are in by putting too much energy into it.
- They can develop an addiction to emotional catharsis, constantly expressing difficult emotions with great intensity just for the sake of it.
- Sometimes they go to extremes, in which everything becomes exaggerated for them. They get caught up in the surface appearances of things or in transitory experiences. They go after experience for its own sake, regardless of the ethics of it, and regardless of how their actions affect others.
- They may experience a feeling of insatiability which leads them to want more and more of the same. This leads to addiction, which is an attempt to mask the emptiness of an internal void.
- They risk becoming addicted to highs and seeking out cheap thrills.
- They often have an inability to concentrate. They are restless and engage in frenzied activity. They have a tendency to go over the top. They can be wild, even violent, changeable and unstable.
- They can behave in ways that are erratic, chaotic, capricious and moody.
- They may try to deny negative feelings and experiences. They attempt to defend themselves against being dragged down out of their state of euphoria.

Archetypal Remedy

These qualities belong archetypally to the remedy Medorrhinum. See the remedy profile on page 203 for what happens when energy gets blocked in those on this path.

The Path of Homemaking

This is the path of making a home and bringing up children. It can be a phase of your life before you go and explore other directions. In Hinduism it is treated as a major part of the life cycle of an individual, which should be fulfilled before moving into the contemplative, religious phase of life. This path is not necessarily about creating an actual family. People on this path may work in caring professions such as health care or education, or perhaps within religious communities, where faith is part of the binding structures that hold people together. They see community as an extension of the extended family structure, containing a network of supportive interconnections.

People who are attracted to this path swap their self-interest for an altruistic concern for the well-being of others. They value sharing and caring for others. They feel that people are far more important than material things. They often have a strong sense of family – regardless of whether their own family unit is conventional or not – and see the integrity of supportive community structures as fundamental to the health of the individual. They use their task of parenting to tend the spark of life in their offspring or in mentoring others. They aim to provide enough support and encouragement to nurture the development of another being, without controlling or stifling the unique path of that being. They develop the ability to set boundaries that provide a safe container for the expectations of others, and a responsive framework for others to go about their life tasks.

Homemakers have a strong sense of what 'family' means, and what every member of the family unit contributes. A sense of belonging and community provides an important underpinning to the life of each person. People attracted to this style of expressing their destiny have a strong sense of what is possible, and what is right, for each person. They facilitate and nurture the strengths and interests of family members through love and understanding.

At the same time they have a flexible openness and an ability to go with the flow, adapting to the changing needs of others. For people on this path, relationships are more important than theories about how they should proceed on the path of home-making.

- People on this path create a resource for others to use as a refuge, haven or retreat.
- They have an ability to listen and respond appropriately to the needs of others.
- They provide a focus for connection, warmth and community.
- They promote the values of sharing and caring.
- They tolerate difference and the unique qualities of others.
- They foster the growth and development of others.
- They provide stability and support.
- They are persistent.
- They often have a highly developed sense of aesthetic appreciation.
- Their giving to other people can be abundant.

NEGATIVE QUALITIES ASSOCIATED WITH THOSE ON THE PATH OF
HOMEMAKING

- They can be too busy doing to just be with others.
- They can become bogged down in material or domestic concerns.
- They can behave in a complacent and unadventurous manner.
- They can become emotionally cold and indifferent to the needs of others.
- They can neglect themselves, living vicariously through others.
- They can become exhausted and burnt out through dutiful giving.
- They can feel frustrated and resentful.
- They may try to manipulate and control others, needing to know where everyone is at all times.
- They revel in a sense of authority and may be tempted to abuse their power.
- They can become rigid about how things should be done.
- They become over-anxious about people they are close to.
- They may suffer anxiety about failing or not being good enough.
- Sometimes people on this path become dependent on others for approval.
- They hate being taken for granted; they need to feel appreciated.

Archetypal Remedy

These qualities belong archetypally to the remedy Calcarea carbonica. See the remedy profile on page 184 for what can happen when energy gets blocked in those on this path.

The Path of Love

The capacity to love and to relate to the soul in others is a sign of deep integration. Through love you can find the unity at the heart of all relationships. This is the path of devotion, through which love can awaken the soul out of its isolation and reconnect it to the rest of humanity. The main impetus is to realize the loving nature of our existence. Once people can access this love, they are motivated to bring the healing power of love into the world. They do this by connecting with the spiritual dimension of life and the soul in others.

The path of love assumes the inter-relatedness of all of us, in such an essential manner that it dissolves ideas of difference and dualism.

The longing for union sets you on a path of searching for meaning through love. Love is the traditional path of mystics, who pursue religious experience as a means of merging with the divine. Mystics, those on the inner contemplative path, say that the universe is pure love. They hold that love is always present, and that you can experience this love so long as you open yourself to it. Love that is based on a spiritual awareness is about experiencing a sense of unity and merging with the beloved. Sufi mystics such as the Persian Jalal-a-din Rumi have penned exquisite devotional poetry about their relationship with God as their Beloved.

People attracted to this path try to create a greater awareness of the fundamental importance of love to humanity. Being on this path requires developing the kind of unconditional open-heartedness to other people that is usually reserved for your lover or your child. The ideal of love only comes alive when you actualize it in daily life. When you are 'in love', you are more aware of the abundant love that is always available. You can use your primary relationship as a vehicle to explore the path of love. This is the purpose of meeting a soul-mate.

People on this path may need to deal with a sense of aloneness and heal any past experience of separation in order to open up to the possibility of merging with their beloved. This merging on the soul level does not make a relationship co-dependent. It is a more spacious way of relating to others which allows each person his or her own space.

When a sense of your own soul comes to the foreground in a relationship, it can provide a path of authenticity, integrity and wholeness. In this case you do not need to wait for your lover to become worthy of being treated as divine: you treat them as if they were already perfect. The art of loving means that you try not to take them for granted or attempt to change them, but instead you worship them as your soul-mate. When you have learned to align yourself to the path of love in your principal relationship, you can extend what you have learned to your relationships with other people. You can treat all relationships as a mirror of the mystical union you experience between lover and beloved.

POSITIVE QUALITIES ASSOCIATED WITH THOSE ON THE PATH OF LOVE

✵ People on this path have an affectionate, giving nature.

✵ They are warm, open and forgiving.

✵ They are responsive and take pleasure in good things that happen to others.

✵ They have a whole-hearted abandonment to devotion and ardour.

✵ They honour and cherish others, and appreciate the ability to love.

✵ They are adaptable, flexible and sociable.

NEGATIVE QUALITIES ASSOCIATED WITH THOSE ON THE PATH OF LOVE

✵ They need love and feel easily spurned if those they love don't place a similar value on the relationship.

✵ They can express their emotional demands in a manipulative way.

✵ They have a tendency to form co-dependent relationships, losing any sense of self or personal space.

Archetypal Remedy

These qualities belong archetypally to the remedy Pulsatilla. See the remedy profile on page 217 for what happens when energy gets blocked in those on this path.

The Path of Reparation

The life task for people aligned with this path is to repair the past by healing old wounds and ensuring that the misdeeds of the past don't re-occur. Their life work is to heal damaging early experiences in their own lives, and those of their parents. Religions that assume re-incarnation would include the need to heal the 'Karmic' effect, or ripples from woundings experienced in past lives. A Christian interpretation would describe the task as being to heal evil or the suffering inflicted on others through the force of evil.

On the path of reparation, one is helping to heal the world of its wounding through healing oneself. The holocaust experience is an obvious example where the pain and suffering inflicted upon earlier generations continues to take its toll on the children of holocaust survivors.

One of my patients, a Jewish man in his forties, described the legacy of guilt he experienced for the mere fact that he was alive. 'Most of my parents' families were wiped out. They met, married and conceived me straight after the war was finished, in an attempt to recreate a family to replace all those family members they had lost. At a deep level I feel I have no right to be here when everyone else was killed. My parents were depressed for a long time, and I know my mother felt so devastated that at times she wanted to die.' For him, the task was to align himself with his will to live, finding acceptance and joy in being alive. This involved accepting an attachment to life, while letting go of a fear of death.

Another of my patients was ritually abused by members of a cult with which her parents were involved when she was a child. Memories of this abuse started resurfacing after the birth of her own child, and she had a nervous breakdown.

Where such experiences have left people very fragile and vulnerable, putting all their focus into healing themselves physically, emotionally and spiritually becomes their life task.

The negative aspects and experiences that we attempt to split off from our conscious awareness are often the very things that need to be integrated psychologically in order to heal and move on in life. Integrating difficult and painful experiences is crucial to making ourselves whole again. It's important to acknowledge all your complex feelings of rage, fear, loss, sadness or powerlessness before moving on to some kind of acceptance.

On the path of reparation, many people find that they need to be able to examine traumatic past experiences, filling in the gaps in their knowledge so that they understand clearly what happened and are able to face the knowledge of all that the experience entailed.

Sharing memories can also be important in the journey towards healing. Finding a community of other people with similar experiences can allow those on this path to open up about what happened, diminishing the power of keeping secrets and releasing buried grief. Talking about their experiences also serves to alert other people to what has happened. Raising the awareness of others about suffering is an important part of trying to prevent such damaging things from happening again and again.

The journey to healing often involves being able to move into a position of witness to what happened, without feeling like a victim. After a period of mourning, people on this path attempt to come to terms with the incomprehensible, and find personal meaning in their own existence.

POSITIVE QUALITIES ASSOCIATED WITH THOSE ON THE PATH OF REPARATION

- They develop tremendous courage and fortitude.
- They develop the ability to feel compassion for their own suffering and to empathize with others.
- They may be tolerant and accepting of others in spite of their failings.
- They are sensitive towards the suffering of others.

꩜ They feel connected with others, recognizing that the fate of one person affects us all.

꩜ They are much more conscious of the possible repercussions of their own actions.

꩜ They stand up against injustice.

꩜ They provide a focus for constructive social change.

NEGATIVE QUALITIES ASSOCIATED WITH THOSE ON THE PATH OF REPARATION

꩜ They get stuck in old emotions, such as anger or sadness about the past.

꩜ They brood about old wrongs, and dwell on the past.

꩜ They may be unable to put their energy into what's happening now.

꩜ They over-identify with victimhood.

꩜ They find it difficult to trust others.

꩜ They feel unsafe and need constant reassurance from others.

꩜ They develop a blaming attitude towards others and find it impossible to consider whether forgiveness might be helpful to their own healing.

Archetypal Remedy

See Natrum muriaticum (page 206) for the picture that can emerge when the energy gets blocked for those on this path.

The Path of Service

The path of service resonates with those individuals who prioritize caring for others. It embodies the Christian principles of loving thy neighbour as thyself and doing unto others as you would like to be done to. People who journey along this route develop a consciousness of suffering and what suffering entails. They aspire to alleviate the suffering of others, through helping them in whatever ways they are able.

Caring for others involves witnessing the experiences and suffering of others and of the world. It is about compassion, feeling love in your heart in the face of others' suffering and sharing their pain. People who follow this path value and care for each and every human being. They work to nurture positive forces in their community and environment.

People on this path are receptive to being a channel for the world of spirit, allowing soul energy to be passed through them rather than drawing on their own personal reserves of energy. This makes their resources seem inexhaustible. They pour out their lives into the collective, offering aid and support to others. They act as mediators and facilitate the development of others.

POSITIVE QUALITIES ASSOCIATED WITH THOSE ON THE PATH OF SERVICE

- People on this path exhibit the positive qualities of caring, which include empathy, compassion, faith and the strength of purpose that gives them the stamina to persist in the face of suffering.
- They possess insight and clarity into what motivates others, and develop great wisdom.
- They are idealistic, but apply their principles in a very practical way. Their fundamental altruism is expressed through companionship, connection and consideration for the needs of others.

NEGATIVE QUALITIES ASSOCIATED WITH THOSE ON THE PATH OF SERVICE

- They end up feeling obligated and may act like martyrs.
- They can become worn out and self-abnegating. They may feel downtrodden or subdued. They risk relating passively to others in ways that are submissive or servile.
- They can become dependent on others.
- They risk losing their sense of self-respect. They are prone to a loss of will and motivation.

✍ The suffering they witness can make them despair of the human condition. They sometimes feel trapped by circumstances, and then they feel bleak, imprisoned and resentful.

✍ They are prone to depression and may experience a lack of joy in their lives.

Archetypal Remedy

These qualities belong archetypally to the remedy Aurum metallicum. See the remedy profile on page 180 for what happens when energy gets blocked in those on this path.

The Path of Social Activism

An idealistic vision of social life orients people on this path towards service for others. They feel strongly that the world should be a better place for everyone, not just those who can help themselves. They feel empathy for those who are disadvantaged, and this motivates them to explore strategies to enable those in need to help themselves. They are attracted to self-help and community-based projects in which their ideals can permeate group networks. Like those on the path of service, their personality is usually empathic and altruistic, which makes these people dedicated and persistent in attempting to make their vision manifest.

This path is concerned with carrying a collective conscience for society. It involves becoming aware of the issues in the life of society that need the attention of individuals with compassionate awareness – the things that local and central government bodies leave unattended. Being on this path requires an ability to empathize with the oppressed and dispossessed as well as a more global awareness than that common among specific interest groups. It involves integrating a personal sense of integrity with the wider social context of life.

Spiritual seeker and writer Andrew Harvey calls it the 'direct path', because it involves uniting political, personal and spiritual dimensions in the service of social good. It involves creating community through bringing an awareness of our union with the divine (comm-union) and our fundamental unity as human beings (comm-unity)

People who follow this path are altruistic and work on behalf of others. They aim to dissolve the sense of alienation in society. They are good at motivating and empowering others. They tend to be idealistic. Through initiating projects they sow the seeds which support communal development. Being an agent for positive social change means learning the task of living in a community through a concern for the key issues of that community. They try to facilitate communication between different interest groups, and are good at networking and forging links between groups and individuals.

There can be a temptation for people on this path to stand against all forms of authority, because they perceive it to be self-serving and hierarchical. In rejecting any involvement with the power games of those in positions of power, they risk rejecting the notion of authority in all its aspects.

The challenge for those aligned with this path is to find inner authority from their own experience rather than from that imposed by institutions or established structures. People who journey along this path may need to find their own voice and speak from the strength of their convictions.

POSITIVE QUALITIES ASSOCIATED WITH THOSE ON THE PATH OF SOCIAL ACTIVISM

- People on this path are fervent, serious and determined in pursuit of their ideals. They are committed to a utopian vision.
- They are selfless and altruistic.
- They are sensitive to injustice.
- They are full of resolve and intent on applying reforms.
- They can be tireless campaigners on behalf of the underprivileged, and are vigilant against any infringement of the rights of others.
- They tend to be visionaries, philanthropists and reformers.
- They are devoted to good causes.
- They are often activists and think in terms of revolutionary proposals.
- They are effective at creating social change.

✿ They persevere and pay careful attention to detail.

✿ Their perceptions become finely tuned so that they develop the ability to cut through trivia or dishonesty.

NEGATIVE QUALITIES ASSOCIATED WITH THOSE ON THE PATH OF SOCIAL ACTIVISM

✿ They are often motivated by anger, which can hamper them from moving towards resolution.

✿ They can take up a combative stance so that they are constantly stirring up conflict.

✿ They find it difficult to negotiate.

✿ They behave in a militant manner and find it hard to back down when necessary.

✿ They become rigid in their thinking, unable to consider flexible responses to a situation in order to achieve the best possible outcome.

Archetypal Remedy

These qualities belong archetypally to the remedy Causticum. See the remedy profile on page 187 for what happens when energy gets blocked in those on this path.

The Path of Transcendence

This is the path of meditation, reflection, contemplation and prayer. The aspiration of people who are attracted to this path is to manifest their inner self through being rather than through doing. They let themselves go into the heart of their life experiences, instead of expending all their effort actively trying to influence the outcome. They prefer to surrender to this process rather than trying to analyse it.

This path is about unifying the spiritual and experiential dimensions of existence and realizing that joy and bliss are direct experiences of the sublime. People on this path aspire to unify the realm of matter and that of their soul. They feel connected, part of a greater whole, because of the glimpses they have of being at one with the universe. Buddhists describe this as getting beyond the world of illusion and entering into the spaciousness of limitless awareness – the spaciousness that is our birthright. They say we can experience it by calming the incessant busy-ness of our small minds.

Those who pursue this path attempt to source wisdom from levels deep inside. They delve into the essence of things to develop a different kind of understanding that comes through non-intellectual faculties.

The challenge for those on this path is to apply their knowledge in the real world in order to make a difference to others. This is the test of whether someone is pursuing transcendence as a self-interested strategy. They need to hold a sense of detachment from the immediate outcome of their actions while also being con-nected with others on the level of our common humanity.

One patient of mine followed Buddhist practices seriously. He spent hours each day in meditation and often went on retreats with various teachers. He shaved his hair and put on the saffron robes worn by monks in Tibet and India. In order to earn a living, he was still working in a health centre, relishing in the opportunity to guide those who came in to browse. He needed help with homeopathic treatment to keep his feet on the ground, as he was finding it difficult reconciling the fact that he had to earn money with his attraction to a dedicated monastic lifestyle.

Being on this path involves being open to spiritual grace and allowing it to manifest itself in the world. The touch of grace is evident in people on this path, so that those they come in contact with are made aware of their own soul.

POSITIVE QUALITIES ASSOCIATED WITH THOSE ON THE PATH OF TRANSCENDENCE

❧ People on this path are often visionaries, seers and diviners.
❧ Those on this path develop qualities of tranquillity and peacefulness.
❧ They tend to be artistic and have a romantic approach to life.
❧ They are sensitive to atmospheres and can read between the lines. They pick up on moods and read body language.

They have a strongly developed sense of intuition.

They are insightful: they can tune in to what motivates other people and pick up on their moods. They are sympathetic and empathetic.

They are enthusiastic and excitable.

They are sensitive and caring to the needs of others.

They can be expansive, with a creative approach to life. Their faculties of imagination and fantasy and their ability to daydream can enrich mundane reality.

They may be vivacious, with bubbly personalities. They are animated and spirited. They are lively, sociable and eager to connect with others. They are open and expressive.

NEGATIVE QUALITIES ASSOCIATED WITH THOSE ON THE PATH OF
TRANSCENDENCE

They can be insubstantial and fanciful. They tend to be escapists who try to avoid real-life issues by constructing a fabulous internal reality, building 'castles in the air'.

They are often too intellectual. Life issues may seem purely abstract to them.

They find it difficult to concentrate. They have butterfly minds and are unable to go into anything in depth. It is difficult to pin down what they really think.

They can be unaware of others. They can become cut off and detached emotionally. As a result of passing so much time in thought, they feel ill at ease in their own bodies.

They are often ungrounded. They suffer from feeling spaced out, and sometimes they have out-of-body experiences. They can be what are sometimes called 'space cadets': that is, they seem to be living on another planet from the rest of us, which makes it very hard to communicate with them.

They may suffer from hypersensitivity and a lack of energy.

preparing for soul work

Archetypal Remedy

These qualities belong archetypally to the remedy Phosphorus. See the remedy profile on page 214 for what can happen when energy gets blocked in those on this path.

The Path of Wisdom

The key task for those who are attracted to this path is to convert knowledge into wisdom. Their journey is from a fascination with intellectual prowess to developing the insightful thought of the sage.

This path attracts those who are natural philosophers, concerned with metaphysics and ethics, and with abstract and scientific thinking. They are good at inventing original ideas, evaluating their possible implications and then disseminating them. Becoming a mentor is often a consequence of aligning oneself to this path.

People on this path make excellent teachers, lighting the visionary spark in others. They enjoy fostering the spirit of enquiry and others' natural curiosity.

The challenge for those on this path is to harness their lofty thoughts to a solid and consistent awareness of discipline. By 'discipline' I refer to having an ethical context for the way they think about things. They can develop a sensitive consideration of the multiple layers of consequence deriving from their ideas and actions.

This path is about raising the level of consciousness through knowledge, in the form of providing inspiration and manifesting a spiritual vision in the world. This involves generating ideas, plans and projects; it also means speculating, theorizing and formulating intentions. It involves thinking through underlying designs and principles. These solid plans can provide templates for others to actualize their visions.

People aligned with this path often develop organic, holistic ways of thinking. They are good communicators with a strong sense of interconnectedness between people, ideas and different levels of existence. They are open to sharing their knowledge and allowing others to build on the work they have done. This attitude stems from a commitment to helping others 'wise up'.

One patient comes to mind as a good example of someone on this path. She runs an international training organization educating health professionals so that they can respond to the demands of the public for a more integrated, holistic approach to health. She has spent her life setting up courses and establishing health centres, promoting better methods of treating those who are ill. She always sees the best qualities in people, and her belief in their abilities brings out their positive attributes. Her enthusiasm generates a great deal of interest and support, and her results are far-reaching. Her projects are almost always very successful, sometimes in unexpected ways.

POSITIVE QUALITIES ASSOCIATED WITH THOSE ON THE PATH OF WISDOM

༺ People on this path often succeed in developing the quality of wisdom.

༺ They are able to find ingenious solutions to problems.

༺ They are open to new ideas and have a sense of endless possibilities.

༺ They are optimistic and idealistic.

༺ They are original and inventive and have an aptitude for lateral thinking.

༺ They can think deeply and penetrate the heart of the matter.

༺ They are often reflective and contemplative.

NEGATIVE QUALITIES ASSOCIATED WITH THOSE ON THE PATH OF WISDOM

༺ They may become overly concerned with dry academic knowledge.

༺ They may be eccentric, cranky, self-centred, egotistical, obsessed and abstracted.

༺ They get stuck in their heads and are unable to integrate their intellect with the wisdom of their heart.

༺ They speak in empty words and procrastinate.

༺ They can be lazy and preoccupied, and they tend to defer important decisions.

༺ They are often opinionated. They can have an inflated opinion of their own thoughts, discoveries and inventions.

preparing for soul work

Archetypal Remedy

These qualities belong archetypally to the remedy Sulphur. See the remedy profile on page 237 for what can happen when energy gets blocked in those on this path.

chapter 5

tracing your core themes

Your psychological state is a map of your energy body. The two mirror each other. Your internal preoccupations express the condition of your energy body, and in turn your energy body is shaped by your thoughts, beliefs and actions. You can therefore use the patterns that you find in your life to detect underlying patterns in your energy body. Once you have discovered these patterns, your core themes, *you can see where your homeopathic remedy needs to be focused.*

Homeopaths believe that each of our energy bodies forms a pattern in which many threads can be clearly discerned. These threads can form a constricted pattern or an expansive design, depending on whether your energy is flowing or stagnant. When the threads form a negative pattern they become tight bonds which restrict and bind you in myriad ways. These knots often correspond to difficult experiences which you have been through in your life, or destructive attitudes which limit you. Constitutional treatment with homeopathy involves untying these bonds.

Often it is just one or two threads that are binding you. These are the core themes which are the source of many areas of imbalance in your life. If you can tease out these threads and free their hold on your life, you can step into a more open space. This is a space of greater personal freedom where you can move forward on your life's journey.

A core theme is a thread which forms a recurring pattern through your life. You can look for your core theme or themes, therefore, by trying to find bold patterns which come up again and again in your life. Are there patterns of behaviour or feeling which recur in particular areas of your life? For example, are there issues which continually crop up in your relationships with other people, be they sexual or familial? Are there patterns which repeat themselves in your relation to work or to your financial affairs? Are there patterns which you know have been shared between the generations of your family?

Think about what has stopped you responding fully to the people and events that surround you. Are there particular emotions which block your ability to respond in the present moment when things happen to you? Emotions like guilt and despair, or the feelings of being unworthy or burnt-out, can block your ability to be in the present moment. Do these same blocks occur again and again?

Think about the situations that make you feel unsettled, distracted, reluctant, afraid, unconfident or angry. Do the same types of situation always produce the same feelings?

Ask your friends and family for their observations and insights. Ask each member of your family to write down how they view you, including your children, if you have any. It is a real learning exercise to see yourself as others see you. Certain themes will be reiterated by each family member in different words. It can be easier for others to pick out the threads which make up the picture of your emotional life than for you to do so yourself.

In order to determine the major themes in your life, I suggest that you write the story of your current situation and the feelings you have responded with. Use this narrative to look at the ways in which you might be reinforcing problematic areas in your life, and pick out the themes that keep recurring. Ask yourself what these problems say about you.

You need not try to recount the whole of your life all at once. Try to focus on one area of life and trace your feelings about one particular issue.

As an example, I have written here about my own recent experience of pregnancy and birth, in order to uncover the difficult areas I needed to resolve. Because of the nature of these experiences, I also asked my mother about her experiences of conception, pregnancy and birth for clues.

During my pregnancy I experienced a profound depression that focused on my fear of being a single mother, as a result of watching my sister struggling on her own for a decade. When my relationship unexpectedly ended within several weeks of my conceiving, I was afraid that I could not cope alone. I experienced intense loneliness and cried a lot. I had feelings of panic, and my fears were so intense that I found myself actively pushing away the support that was available to me.

My depression evaporated completely once my son was born, but it has left a legacy of sensitivity to abandonment which I expect will come up later in his life. I believe the depression had to do with issues passed through the generations. I felt that the feelings were so intense that they could not all be mine, and intuitively recognized that some must stem from my mother's experiences during her pregnancy with me, and those of her mother's pregnancy with her.

My mother's relationship also broke down at the time of her pregnancy with me. She felt panicky during the labour and was terrified of giving birth alone. She was actually left alone by staff on the birthing table at the hospital, and fixated on worrying how she would manage to get off the high table and find some scissors to cut the cord, which she believed was necessary to keep me alive.

My own relationship broke up in early pregnancy, and my labour was unexpectedly difficult: I laboured at home with an obstetrician friend for over 30 hours before transferring to hospital. I wept bitter tears of disappointment and fear when I arrived at the maternity ward, only to be left alone for over an hour in an exhausted state. 'This feels exactly how my pregnancy has felt all along!' I wept, feeling totally alone.

I was astonished to learn that my mother's mother had also had a precarious time during her pregnancy. She had tremendous problems carrying her babies to term, and had had so many miscarriages that she was advised to have a termination when she became pregnant with my mother. Instead she ran away, hiding out until the pregnancy was too far advanced for any medics to intervene. Because giving birth was dangerous for her, I imagine she must also have been very scared.

The experiences of the women in my family are about our feeling unsupported when faced with the frightening experience of giving birth. When we are in a situation where we can no longer control things, we have an experience of being profoundly let down. This is what I experienced when I found myself giving birth alone. Not only had my partner left me, but I'd ended up with an emergency caesarian instead of a home waterbirth. I felt let down by my treatment in hospital; it was so appalling that I made a formal complaint. I was also let down by the friend who had ostensibly come to look after me in my hour of need. The final straw was when my home help left after only 10 days; I cried so despairingly and for so many hours that I felt on the verge of a nervous breakdown.

Because my core theme was one of feeling let down on every side, my homeopath prescribed the remedy Pulsatilla, which helped me move through my feelings of utter abandonment and accept my life as a single mother. Now that I have dealt with my fears for my son because he has only one parent, I can say I actively enjoy my life and I have opened up to love again.

In order to discover our spiritual lesson from any difficult situation we are in, we need to ask ourselves a question: 'What can I learn from this particular situation?' One of the lessons I had to learn was that things improve only when I start actively to look for and accept support. Because I've always been so independent (as a result of being convinced that my needs for emotional support would not be met), I had to learn to let go of any notion of self-sufficient struggle. When I started to accept love and allow it to flow, my life opened to joy.

It is not easy to uncover the core themes of our lives. Because each of us has strong feelings about our life experiences and how they affect us, it is difficult to look at our own story and understand the message behind it. We might be astute at perceiving what is going on in the lives of our friends and relatives, but we usually have a blind spot about our own core problems. If we could see our own underlying problems easily, we would probably have resolved them and moved on!

Even with years of experience as a homeopath, I can find it difficult to analyse myself and my own situation in a dispassionate, unbiased way. I recognize that I need the help of a homeopathic colleague to prescribe a remedy which will help unblock the situation and release the learning for me. Taking the insights about your current situation and sharing them with an experienced homeopath will facilitate your path towards healing.

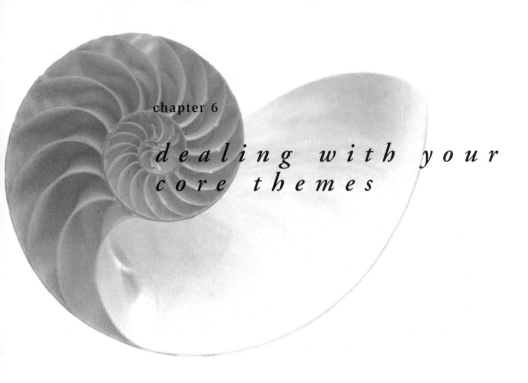

dealing with your core themes

In this chapter I shall discuss common psychological problems which form the core themes *running through different people's lives. For each problem I shall explain how homeopathy understands the problem and how it recommends we deal with it.*

Dealing with these problems is not just a matter of finding the right homeopathic remedy. For each problem I shall mention some changes you can make yourself which will help you overcome these difficulties, suggesting a possible *learning for the soul* for each of the challenging issues discussed.

For each problem I shall also present in detail the case of one of the people I have worked with, describing how the problem affected different aspects of his or her life and how a particular remedy was of help. I shall also mention a few other possible remedies of the many which can be used to treat each problem, so that you are aware that in homeopathic treatment there are a whole range of remedies which might be needed to treat a particular problem. The art of homeopathic prescribing is to discuss and analyse all aspects of each problem with the patient, in order to select the most effective remedy.

Addiction

Addiction to behavioural patterns often rests on blaming others for what is not right in your own life, in order not to take the responsibility for the quality of it yourself. This makes it difficult to be really honest about yourself. The belief that life is miserable can be just as much an addiction as smoking cannabis constantly: both habits are means of avoiding becoming what you could be. What you need is to develop maturity, but this is made difficult by the addictive behaviours which stop you having to take responsibility.

On one level, addiction is an escape from the truth of your own being. You are afraid to look inside yourself because of the fear that you are completely empty.

This is what Rory, a man in his late thirties, described as the key to his addictive personality:

'I felt very empty a lot of the time, so I used to drink, smoke dope, and take ecstasy tablets every weekend when I went clubbing. I started trying heroin. I know if I had been more depressed the drugs would have taken hold of me. I have always felt I didn't fit in anywhere. As a child I was convinced that I did not belong to my family because I had been adopted. I never felt accepted by my community. I can see now that I took drugs to try to escape this feeling of isolation, but the drugs just made me more depressed and insular. During the come-down afterwards, I would plummet into a black hole.

'Finally I accepted the thought that I needed help. As soon as I accepted that, I found the strength to change. I realized I had to do something pretty dramatic, so I just stopped using everything. I'd always been interested in spirituality, and

Buddhism resonated most closely with my own beliefs. Following Buddhist practices has helped me accept my aloneness and even see it in a positive light.'

Addiction is often the result of a compulsive defence against some kind of emotional pain that feels unbearable. The process of splitting off parts of your personality often leads to fragmentation, so you may end up with a personality that is on the borderline of not holding together in one piece. Drugs, other substances or experiences – whatever you are addicted to – make you feel good for a period of time and block out the pain. It is difficult to let go of something that gives you pleasure in order to face unalloyed pain.

Some users of psychoactive drugs such as LSD claim that drugs can open their consciousness to the spiritual dimensions of life. As a homeopath, I hear much more about how 'bad trips' have left a legacy of paranoia, sometimes verging on madness. In cases like this, homeopaths sometimes use specific remedies made from the drug involved in an addiction, to clear out de-stabilizing after-effects.

Since the 1960s the idea that a drug-induced religious experience is the same as an authentic one has encouraged people to explore the use of mind-altering substances. They have been used from time immemorial and are still used in traditional societies to facilitate altered states of consciousness, but usually in a ritual setting with a shaman taking care of the soul. The contemporary use of drugs, whether street drugs, pharmaceuticals or social drugs like alcohol, seems to me a lazy way of pursuing a change of awareness. It is lazy in that you are choosing to take the easy option of instant pleasure over genuine happiness, immediate gratification over long-term gain. Instead you can foster an authentic transformation by developing a sense of the sacred in everyday life.

The Tibetan spiritual leader the Dalai Lama emphasizes that the activities we are involved in should have long-term benefits for ourselves and others; this is what creates real happiness. For those on a spiritual path it is important how we choose to make use of our lives and our bodies. What counts is what you are doing in life, not whether you feel pleasure or satisfaction. Work is ultimately important not as an occupation, but as a means of contributing something meaningful to others. You need to engage your energies fully rather than stay a passive observer. Life is a flow, and if you do not move forward you will stagnate. This lack of engagement can be about blocked creativity.

The Buddhist and Hindu spiritual traditions talk about 'right thinking' as a prerequisite for 'right action'. Right thinking means paying attention to fundamental ethics rather than pursuing whims. The path to healing addiction is through action. You need to manifest your search for soul in your drive to be effective in the world.

Maureen, a glamorous young woman, came to see me complaining that she could not focus her considerable talents properly. She had a highly paid job and was obviously bright and vivacious. She got bored easily and needed a lot of stimulation. For years she had had a hectic lifestyle that involved lots of drugs, drinking and sex. She was currently in a relationship based on convenience rather than love, which she said suited her because she preferred not to make an emotional commitment.

She had a bubbly, fun-loving, dynamic personality, but complained of feeling that she was living her life at half-mast. She had never had to work hard, because things always came easily to her. She lacked discipline and felt blocked creatively. She said she wanted to sing but just could not practise regularly. 'I can pursue other creative pursuits like dancing, because they are not really important to me.' She was clearly afraid to try in case she might fail, and distracted herself with having a good time.

Underneath was a strong sense of inadequacy, which Maureen described as a fear of being rejected which dated from childhood. Sadly there was a history of abuse, which had left her feeling angry, upset and ashamed.

I prescribed the homeopathic remedy Medorrhinum because of Maureen's tendency to distract herself from her emotional distress with substances or transient sexual escapades, which in the long run only undermined her sense of self-worth and made her feel more shame.

When she came back for her second visit, she reported, 'I feel so much better not drinking and have followed the detox diet you gave me. I think drinking was a way of numbing myself. My own feelings are strong. Usually I get very emotional when other people are upset, and I realize that's because it's easier to experience things second hand.'

The remedy enabled Maureen to look at her difficult feelings about her father. 'He just talks a lot about himself and doesn't listen. I realized that in spite of everything

I had to tell my father that I do love him, and I had to hear him tell me he loves me. We've actually been able to do this. I was able to forgive him for hitting me, and he actually apologized for his violence. As a result, I've been feeling less insecure around him. I realized that has been the basis of my feelings of insecurity.'

She ended her relationship with her boyfriend, which she admitted was basically self-serving, and eventually gave up her job and moved back to her home town. She enrolled in a voice training programme, using the self-development work on the course as a way of integrating parts of herself. Through working on her personality traits, Maureen began to unblock her creativity.

In learning to love herself, she realized that she needed to rediscover how to act with integrity. 'In the past if someone was nasty to me I would be equally nasty back. I'm more conscious of this now and am working on changing it so that I can just get on with what I want to do.'

OTHER POSSIBLE REMEDIES IN STATES OF ADDICTION

Avena sativa	a tonic for those who are weak and thin as a result of too many drugs. When used along with a good diet, it helps strengthen the body.
Capsicum	for people of a melancholic disposition who feel nostalgic for the past, when life was better. They drink in an attempt to alleviate their depression.
Nitrous oxide	indicated for people who feel totally ungrounded, becoming disoriented, light-headed and giggly
Nux moschata	used for people who feel mentally disoriented as a result of drug use. They describe feeling confused and drowsy – Nux moschata has been used to treat narcolepsy, a condition of uncontrollable sleepiness.
Nux vomica	helps people who drink because they can't bear to be alone with themselves. Also for alcoholics who become aggressive or abusive when drunk.
Opium	helps users of heroin and opiates rebalance their ravaged energy pattern. They feel separate from others; at times blissfully self-contained, at others manipulatively calculating.

Sulphur	for those with an intellectual approach to the use of drugs, who become garrulous and philosophical when under the influence. It is also helpful where energy is depleted because of a toxic liver.

Soul Lesson for Addiction

To discover the truth of your own self and how to live in accordance with that truth.

Anger

Anger can alert us to the fact that we are going beyond our limits. It can erupt when we feel something is wrong and our personal boundaries are being infringed. But sometimes anger is a sign of our preciousness, when we feel that someone has personally affronted us. In this instance, it is a result of egotism. All too often we give credence to a personal sense of affront, which is often about offended pride or vanity. Feeling insulted or easily offended is a result of an excessive concern with the self and how other people perceive us. Violent anger is a symptom of pent-up rage, erupting in destructive ways. If you feel violent, it is always a sign that you need professional help.

Most people attribute anger to excessive stress. However, the term 'stress' is not always helpful because it is used in such generalized and simplistic ways. Stress is a very broad concept that covers a multitude of causes, and is simply a label to describe an overstimulation of the nervous system rather than the complexities of each individual's coping strategies. What is important to a homeopath is not so much the stressful things that have occurred in your life, but how you have responded to these challenges.

Often people are afraid to express their anger because it feels too risky. However, when you learn how to express anger safely you realize that other people are not psychologically demolished by hearing what you say. A homeopathic remedy such as Nux vomica will enable you to express your anger, not in violent outbursts but by gently releasing pent-up feelings and allowing you to verbalize your feelings more appropriately. The machismo aspect of anger often compensates for real or imagined deficiencies in your character, but after taking your appropriate remedy you will feel more confident and have less need to prove yourself.

The husband of a friend was in the manic phase of manic depression, ranting day and night without sleeping and behaving very provocatively. He reveled in his fearful state of confusion. He did not see it as a trap, until severe depression took over from his manic psychosis. He was a Sufi, and it was interesting to me how his community attempted to contain his psychosis without having him hospitalized. The religious leader described his illness as an example of inflated egoism and emphasized how much all of our egos are extremely disturbed because of living in a society which values individualism over and above spiritual purpose.

Ego is a notion coined by psychoanalysts to describe that self-interested part of us that constructs an identity in the world. Psychotherapy tends to engage with the ego, trying to strengthen it by making us more aware of the components of our identity. Because Western European and American society has been very much influenced by psychotherapy's world view, we regard a strong ego as a good thing and look askance at those without a clear sense of self. Conversely, in most spiritual teachings a concern with self-identity is seen as a limiting illusion, because it doesn't spring from a spiritual perspective. Spiritual teachings try to challenge attitudes and habits that limit us; they try to encourage ways of living that enable us to become more aware.

From a spiritual perspective, life is constant change and any difficulties we have in accepting change can be viewed as opportunities for learning and for spiritual growth. So anyone getting stuck in one particular response is by definition limited, and these stuck responses need to be examined and transformed.

The Dalai Lama says that anger can be constructive when it's harnessed to social activism. He recommends using the righteous power of your anger to 'ride the bull' – use it as a constructive force to right wrongs.

Aziz was referred to me by his counsellor. He came to see me two weeks before he was due to have surgery for Crohn's disease, a condition in which the intestines are chronically inflamed and ulcerated. A piece of his intestine had been removed 10 years previously, but he had been subject to regular attacks over the intervening years. These episodes usually came on when he was under stress. He struggled a lot with anger, which he rarely let out. His father had terrorized the family with his fits of rage, and as a child Aziz had learned that it was just not safe to express his own anger. He always felt better when he did get so worked up that the anger spilled out, but most of the time he managed to keep a lid on it. He felt frustrated about working in a family business because he was unable to make independent decisions, and also about his marriage, especially sexually. He said that he needed sex to feel good about himself: it was like a tension release. His desire for sex was obsessive, and he had a mistress.

Bottling up his emotional reactions to stress led to panic attacks and feelings of depersonalization, episodes in which he felt he wasn't present in his body. At other times his body was taken over by sensations in the nerves that shot up from his abdomen into his head. 'I seem very calm, but underneath I'm a seething mess.'

His remedy, Nux vomica, improved his abdominal pain so much that he decided to delay surgery. In fact, he never ended up going for surgery, because doses of Nux vomica at infrequent intervals healed his ulcerated bowel. His bowel movements and digestion improved as a result. Even better, the remedy made him feel calmer so that he no longer suffered bouts of nerve irritation.

He was still moody and irritable, however, and admitted that he found it difficult sharing his inner world. He said he still felt like a failure and mourned the wasted opportunities of his life. He was in a mid-life crisis, looking for a purpose – something he could call his own and do for himself.

After a major row, his rocky marriage broke apart and he moved out into a flat alone. He oscillated between fuming and feeling devastated by his wife's rejection. He found being alone almost intolerable.

My most immediate task was to ameliorate his panic about being alone. Once again Nux vomica helped Aziz to deal with his rage and fear, which left him more aware of his loss and longing for his wife. I encouraged him to stay in the flat rather than rushing around in an attempt to fill up the emptiness with meaningless activity.

It was very hard for him to do so, and his old pattern of assuaging his emotional needs with sex led him into casual encounters. At this stage I gave him Medorrhinum, which rebalances the need for immediate gratification against pursuing a course that will ultimately be more fulfilling.

Aziz needed many repeats of his constitutional remedy, Nux vomica, to help him deal with his anger throughout the process of negotiating a divorce settlement. The remedy enabled him to feel more accepting once he had dealt with his rage, and he was able to acknowledge his own part in undermining the relationship. He enrolled on a course of study, determined to pursue his own interests while carrying on with work. He recognized how important it was for him to find a meaningful channel for his agile mind and enquiring soul.

OTHER POSSIBLE REMEDIES

Anacardium	indicated where the person is feeling cold anger and comes out with caustic comments. Such people may refuse to relent or back down from their position.
Bryonia	for those who feel touchy and easily irritated, who repeatedly say they prefer their own space and want to be left alone
Causticum	indicated where suppressed anger from the past finds expression in political anger, but in ways that may be ultimately damaging to oneself and others
Chamomila	a good remedy for those who are intolerant of physical pain or discomfort, becoming impetuous, emotional and bad-tempered
Hepar sulphur	helps insecure and vulnerable people who erupt in an abusive rage when their security is threatened
Medorrhinum	recommended for people who tend to fly off the handle and lash out physically. People in this remedy pattern may break things or kick the dog in a fit of temper.
Moschus	used for people who suffer asthma attacks as a consequence of a build-up of anger
Nitric acid	helpful for those who are habitually in a negative mood. It is good for people who are pessimistic and bad-tempered,

especially in the morning when they feel they do not want to face the day.

Soul Lesson for Anger

In order to deal with challenges with patience and equanimity, you need to develop tolerance and compassion towards others.

Anxiety

Anxiety is where we worry about possible negative outcomes rather than maintaining an attitude of optimism and trust in our own capacity to cope with whatever comes our way. In this way anxiety limits us, and we dare not take risks. Our lives can become circumscribed by fears.

Sometimes this attitude is engendered by our parents always telling us not to do things for fear of what might happen to us. At other times it is to do with an over-identification with various troublesome experiences we may go through in life. This habit of fastening attention onto the negative can become a way of life. Negative emotions sap energy, whereas joy and laughter nurture us.

Anxiety is endemic in contemporary society. Our emotional antennae are primed to respond to the pace of life with panic. Living as we do under tremendous stress, we are easy prey. Anxiety appears in different forms: the adrenaline state of rushing to meet demands and deadlines, the mental agitation of insomnia, or the neurotic feelings behind hypochondria. Anxiety about health can become a major obsession, with concern over symptoms often masking the real anxiety, which is about mortality.

Many people expend a lot of effort searching for medical answers rather than trying to solve the cause of their neurotic anxiety. In the 1950s, doctors created drug addiction by prescribing tranquillizers like Valium for years on end. The 1980s heralded 'the Prozac generation', where people prefer to take antidepressants to take the edge off their feelings (positive as well as negative) rather than making changes or finding better ways of dealing with their problems.

I see obsessive compulsive disorder as another response to a fear of chaos or disintegration. By attempting to control aspects of daily experience in a ritualistic and superstitious way, people with this disorder are attempting to control the boundaries of their experience by not letting in anything untoward. By compulsively washing the hands or obsessively checking whether the cooker has been turned off, possible sources of contamination or danger are being fended off. In this state it is impossible to respond to the demands of life with any flexibility, since doing so might invite risks which could, in the opinion of a person in this state, have disastrous consequences. It is this 'what if?' attitude that limits our responses and therefore our experiences.

Ellie would get overwrought about the difficulties she faced being a single mother with a very demanding child. She found it difficult to set and maintain clear boundaries, and her son responded by refusing to obey her, particularly around the issue of sleep. He threw frequent tantrums, which got worse each time another nanny or au pair left their flat. Ellie had high standards, and the relationship with these young women usually went badly wrong within a short time. Her child refused to connect with any of these carers. Working at home and having to meet high outgoings was a constant strain for Ellie, and she was getting more and more tired after years of broken sleep. When she tried to get some rest, her mind would dwell on her financial problems and the pressure of work and deadlines. This anxiety would build up into a state of virtual panic, and if she had to travel abroad for work the fear that she might die and leave her son motherless was such a concern that it created acute panic episodes. The pressure of her sole responsibility for her child meant that the thought of her possible death became obsessional whenever she was under a lot of pressure.

Ellie's remedy was Arsenicum album, which instantly broke the cycle of panic and insomnia, allowing her to deal with the causes of her anxiety in a constructive way: for instance, it gave her the energy to finish a major piece of work and to deal with the tax department. The remedy enabled her to sleep before a plane trip, so that she was not getting so tired worrying about arrangements that she could not then be effective. It enabled her to get on the plane, whereas previously the panic had been so intense that she'd felt she could not even step onto the plane.

Ellie took the remedy at less frequent intervals over the years, whenever practical pressures pushed her into her old habitual response of worrying. Gradually, the remedy allowed her to learn a different way of dealing with her stressful circumstances. By maintaining a more positive and effective frame of mind, Ellie was able to learn a different way of approaching life which allowed her to feel more at peace.

OTHER REMEDIES

Agaricus	for a crippling fear of cancer. People who need this remedy can become quite morbid because their anxiety about health leads them to believe they will die 'before their time'.
Argentum nitricum	indicated for obsessive disorder, panic attacks, claustrophobia and agoraphobia. People in this remedy pattern are easily overwhelmed by feelings of panic, becoming restless and agitated. They find it impossible to stop their minds running over improbable disaster scenarios.
Gelsemium	helpful where a fear of failure creates panic just before interviews or exams
Iodum	used for those who are anxious with an overstimulated mind. People in this remedy pattern may have an overactive thyroid gland, resulting in them feeling hot and sweaty and needing to eat a lot. They feel hurried, harassed and agitated.
Leuticum	used where people feel dirty or contaminated. They are afraid of disease and may wash their hands compulsively.
Psorinum	helps to heal the fear of poverty or 'poverty consciousness'. People in this remedy pattern have low expectations and feel dissatisfied and miserable; they think nothing will ever get better and that this is their lot in life.
Rhus toxicodendron	useful for people who have superstitions behaviour patterns, such as not stepping on cracks in the pavement or compulsively checking that everything electrical is turned off in the house.

Silica	a good remedy for those who feel shy and unconfident, and who withdraw into their own private world whenever they feel exposed in public settings.
Tarentula hispanica	indicated where the person is suffering from hyperactivity or workaholism. People in this energy pattern are impatient and intolerant of other people; they cannot delegate at all. They feel driven inside and find it impossible to relax. They may listen to loud music or indulge in wild dancing to let off steam.

Soul Lesson for Anxiety

Experiment with letting go of your need to control your life in order to learn how to accept change.

Burnout

Burnout occurs most commonly to those in the caring professions and to those of us who take a caring approach to whatever it is we are doing in our life. At some point our spirit of generosity may dry up; we feel that we have not got anything to spare. Instead of operating from a principle of abundance, we find ourselves economizing with our energy, thinking that there is just too little to go around. We feel stretched too thinly and snap back into ourselves. We no longer feel recharged by giving; instead, we feel drained. We may also feel defensive, and react by putting up walls and barriers in an attempt to stop our energy leaking out.

Energy might be dissipated because of the ways our own emotional problems can get stirred up during our attempts to care for others. Sometimes it is due to an overload of negativity and problems which erodes our optimism; at other times it is due to a crisis of conscience, when we are no longer sure we are doing the right thing.

Whatever the reason, problems suddenly become burdens and we feel the strength of our own needs. Our burnout is telling us that we can no longer leave those needs on the back burner. They must be attended to.

At the time I consulted homeopath George Vithoulkas as a patient, I had worked nonstop for many years as a homeopath, and when my live-in relationship broke down I reacted in all the wrong ways, throwing myself into work to distract myself from the emotional crisis. This strategy has a way of tripping you up, usually by making you ill. Since I am pretty hardy constitutionally, what happened to me was burnout. I worked harder and harder, got more and more exhausted, and took more holidays with less beneficial effect, until things got so bad I could hardly get up in the mornings and was too exhausted to dress. I could not face the thought of hearing one more problem, which is not how I usually feel about the privilege of sharing people's life stories and discovering the surprising and creative ways they deal with their challenges.

I needed to be busy so that I did not have enough time to think about or feel my emotional pain. It was only after I received my homeopathic remedy that I could create space in my life by letting go of everything I was doing. I cut away from my moorings by going to Egypt for a year, and found that I could be more open to change. Once your intentions are aligned with your deepest desires, it can be amazing how easily things fall into place and your energy starts to flow unimpeded.

Claire is a lively, effusive person who is full of enthusiasm for life. She has been a single mother for many years and enjoys a close relationship with her two children, both of whom have just left home. Her love life has been very troublesome, although she is a romantic and gives a lot to her relationships with men. For many years she was in a functional marriage, which provided a stable environment for raising her daughters but starved her of real emotional connection.

For over 10 years Claire has been involved with a man who cannot fully commit himself to her. She loves him passionately and longs to make a life together with him, but he cherishes what he calls his 'freedom', including the opportunity to have casual sex wherever his work takes him. A decade of this relationship has dashed her hopes, but she is as deeply in love with him as ever, even if her love is now tinged with fatalism.

Claire's colleagues describe her as motherly, but that is an inadequate description of her strengths in her working life. She has a responsible job in management, and has always been an inspirer, facilitator and mediator, enthusing other people with her energy and optimism. She always sees the best in others and strives to encourage them. But again, Claire has not always been lucky in working where she is most appreciated. Although she is wonderful when working closely with a company director – someone more solid who can focus on the kind of detail she finds boring – she has never found a niche where she can soar. She feels that she missed the boat years earlier when she stopped working with an artistic crowd who had given her the stimulation she needed. Her soul gets thirsty as well, and the down side of being seen as the person who gives everyone else strokes is that others tend not to see her own deep need for affirmation and praise.

Claire's burnout happened at a time when she felt totally invisible at work – taken for granted and clearly unappreciated. I prescribed Phosphorus (see page 214) because the bubbly energy that Claire exudes when things in her life are going well had become so depleted that she was on three months' sick leave and confined to bed. Without seeing the positive image of herself that others held up before her, she could not sustain a sense of her own vibrancy.

The remedy stimulated Claire's energy quickly and dramatically, getting her out of bed within a few days. She was able to start sorting out her situation in a radical way.

She needed to create a situation in which to be properly appreciated. If you know yourself and what makes your soul soar, the problem then is how to find a way to express yourself so that you don't have to clip your wings to fit your cage.

After evaluating her strengths and weaknesses, Claire realized that she had to leave her job in order to find something more nourishing. She took the risk of being left with nothing and went through a lot of anxious job-hunting in a very competitive employment climate that was biased against mature women in particular. She knew how good she was, yet at times she found it difficult to hang on to her sense of self-esteem in the absence of any validation. Learning to value oneself is a big challenge for those needing Phosphorus, and the remedy helps you to draw on your own inner resources rather than looking for external validation.

The same issue was relevant in Claire's personal life. She needed to internalize a sense of her own worth so that she did not have to seek it through a range of relationships. She had spent a lot of her life looking after others, both as a wife and mother and in her jobs supporting, facilitating and mentoring others. She was also very considerate in her relationships with men, always trying to make her partner feel cherished. What she needed to learn was simply to cherish herself.

In a mate she needed someone who could meet her need for connection and intensity. The time she spent with her partner was not enough to satisfy her and left her feeling needy and at times desperate with a sense of something missing. Although she kept telling herself she should leave this man, she believed that the challenge for her soul in this relationship was to learn to relish the present rather than dwelling on what she was not getting. However, finally she realized that this man would never be able to meet her on a soul level and she was able to let go.

OTHER REMEDIES

Cocculus	may be needed where people are overanxious about loved ones. They may be exhausted as a result of nursing someone or having broken sleep for months, feeling dizzy and disoriented as a result.
Gelsemium	used where the person feels physically weak. They are so fatigued they can barely climb an escalator, and they like to slump in a chair. Any stress causes an anxiety state, accompanied by trembling.
Muriatic acid	used for people who become ill as a result of their exhaustion. They suffer from fever for several days and can't get their energy back afterwards.
Phosphoric acid	recommended for when people collapse, feeling mentally flat, lifeless and apathetic. They feel too drained to respond emotionally.
Sepia	used when burnout creates an emotional coldness or indifference to loved ones
Stannum	used for people who become ill every time they stop an intense period of work. They are wiped out after any respiratory infection such as bronchitis or pneumonia.

preparing for soul work

Soul Learning for Burnout

Learn how to give from the right orientation. Not at the expense of your own needs, but by ensuring that you feel fulfilled yourself, so that helping others does not drain your own personal energy. In this way, you become a conduit for transpersonal energy.

Confusion

Confusion arises when you feel you have lost your way or perhaps have not yet found it. Not having a clear idea of your path makes it difficult to feel a sense of identity, so that you look to external labels for definition.

Confusion can be exacerbated by an inability to sort through all the influences and pressures in your life, to cut through all the peer and media messages into the heart of your own experience. All this input creates a sensory overload that can distract you from the need to investigate more essential aspects of life.

It is confusing to try to sort out emotional problems by thinking about and analysing them rather than fully entering into your experience. The Christian philosophy of dedicating yourself to God doesn't guarantee that God will take care of you or remove suffering or pain. Confusion arises because we have not yet found another framework for understanding any horrific experiences we might undergo. New Age philosophy emphasizes that everyone is ultimately good, but this may seem a denial of the all too real evil in the world. It is hard to understand or accept the horrors of wars, murder, abuse and exploitation. We all know the good guys do not always win. In fact they are often persecuted, ridiculed, or just unappreciated. So doing the right thing is no insurance policy against suffering. We need to develop the ability to make choices without having a clear indication or guarantee of outcomes. We need to do what seems appropriate without bargaining with life by saying, 'If I do this, I will get that.' Furthermore, we cannot hope to understand fully the meaning of everything we see around us. Once we accept this unknowability, it is less confusing.

Karen, a woman of 39, came to see me because of frequent headaches and exhaustion. She had been knocked out by glandular fever and complained of being easily tired, although she worked long hours as a freelance journalist.

She held a lot of tension in her body, almost like armour: her teeth were constantly clenched and she suffered from backache, nerve pain in the upper arms and bouts of repetitive strain injury. Her face appeared twisted because, as well as a lot of tension in her facial muscles, she had a droopy eyelid and a squint.

She complained of getting confused and easily lost. Her memory was poor. She was dyslexic and transposed words even when speaking. She said that she sometimes felt 'loopy'. She was unconfident because of all this and was afraid of not coping. She felt she could not articulate fast enough, as if she did not know what her opinions were on any subject.

As a child, Karen used to cry whenever she was unable to express her feelings. Her mother had called her a weed, and even now Karen found it difficult to stand up to people. Her character was tremendously emotionally sensitive.

She had reached a crisis in her marriage of 20 years. She was re-evaluating the relationship, but her husband refused to talk about what was distressing her. Two years previously, she had awakened in a state of severe depression and had to be helped out of bed. That was the point at which she became aware that the relationship was stuck and that her deeper needs were not being addressed. In the past she had felt ambivalent about having children, but now her biological clock was ticking loudly. Her husband was quite clear that he did not want their lifestyle to change. Her doctor responded by putting her on the antidepressant Prozac, but she did not find it helpful.

Helleborus is a remedy given for paralysed energy patterns where people feel as if they are in hell, for whatever reason. It corresponds to an energy pattern that disturbs the functioning of the nervous system, resulting in muscle spasm and pain. It was a chronic irritation of the nervous system which produced the distortion of Karen's facial muscles. Cranial osteopaths often see this kind of disturbed pattern in babies after traumatic births, which affect the musculo-skeletal and nervous systems. When given to people whose whole energy pattern corresponds to this remedy, Helleborus calms the irritated nervous system, releasing the knotted muscles and allowing energy to move through the central nervous system again. When

preparing for soul work

needing this remedy, people often describe a gap between sensory input and reaction, as if the information normally passed across the synapses (gaps) between nerve fibres is blocked. Karen described this as a gap between her experiences and her emotional reactions, in which she struggled to find her responses and even to know what was true for her.

Helleborus cleared up her headaches, gave Karen much more energy, and focused her mind. There was a definite, but slow, improvement in the jaw tension, and her face seemed less scrunched up. Her peripheral vision improved also: she had complained that her vision used to 'grey out' when she was tired. Her depression slowly cleared. Under the action of the remedy, Karen felt there was less of a gap between awareness and reaction when she was criticized. 'I feel more able to react at the time, rather than having to go away and wait for it to hit me later.' This is part of the deep healing work the remedy manifests, allowing the person to connect the different facets of themselves. As a more whole being, you can respond in an integrated way – which also demands more integrity from others.

Karen still found it difficult to articulate an urgent need clearly. But as she became less confused, she became more obsessive about the question of whether she wanted children or not. 'I wish I knew,' she complained. It was important for her to pursue the possibility of becoming pregnant, but her husband remained intransigent. Karen felt that it was important to have a choice about whether to have a baby: even though she was not 100 per cent sure herself, she felt that his refusal even to consider it left her with no choice but to weigh up a range of stark options. These included leaving the marriage in order to find another partner, to have a baby on her own, or to stay and bury her anger. This last option was proving impossible. Her speculations got wilder and wilder. She even fantasized about going to a private clinic for artificial insemination.

She was clearly destabilized by the enormity of the issue and her inability to know what she really wanted. Whereas it had been difficult for her to express her feelings, now she was able to feel angry at her husband and upset at her feelings of powerlessness. Instead of collapsing passively into a state of depression, she was now in a more open rebellion. Under the action of the remedy, Karen moved out of her anesthetized emotional state. Instead of suppressing her dissatisfaction, she had needed to feel her anger about her powerlessness. Then she needed to explore her own ambivalence fully in order to arrive at a position which reflected her true feelings. Ultimately, she would have to reach a decision she would be happy about. Helleborus energized her and accelerated this whole process.

OTHER REMEDIES

Alumina	used where the mind feels very slow and dull. People in this remedy pattern find it difficult to think and have to ponder questions for some time before coming up with a response. They are confused and disoriented and feel distressed by this loss of mental acuity.
Anacardium	for people who are extremely indecisive: they usually feel torn in two directions and are unable to decide on one course or another. They get stuck in this state of irresolution.
Calcarea carbonica	good for people who feel that their mental powers have let them down, although they have great powers of perseverance and continue working at understanding or learning something until they get there.
Graphites	a good remedy for people who find it difficult to concentrate and feel as if they are slow mentally. These people are thick-skinned, but they feel frustrated by an inability to comprehend subtle nonverbal information or the indirect ways other people have of communicating.
Plumbum	indicated where people have a poor memory and find it difficult to express themselves. They are slow to take things in and digest them. They may also be self-centred, and find it difficult to put themselves in anyone else's shoes.
Sulphur	helpful where people have worn themselves out mentally and are no longer able to make the quick, creative mental connections they once could.

preparing for soul work

Soul Learning for Confusion

You need to find clarity. In order to express your own truth, you first have to find it within yourself. This means staying with your core issue until you have reached some kind of resolution.

Depression

When you are no longer getting pleasure or satisfaction out of the things that usually make you happy, you might be suffering from depression. Being unable to solve major problems can destabilize us, leaving us susceptible to anxiety, depression and fear. Feelings of pointlessness, helplessness or hopelessness are the hallmarks of depression. It also encompasses feelings such as worthlessness, guilt or even suicide.

You might need to acknowledge these distressing feelings, because they can also have a positive function – they can push you to make constructive changes in your life. The worse you are feeling, the more fundamental or far-reaching might be the changes that you need to make. Practical changes are definitely needed if depression is due to conflicts in your relationship or a rotten work situation.

Depression can be reactive (in reaction to a particular situation) or endogenous (internal), perhaps caused by unresolved issues from your early life or deep feelings masked by business and activity. Suppressing feelings, such as anger, often result in depression. If you feel depressed as a result of internalized anger, after taking your remedy you may become more aware of anger at the same time as your mood improves. The same process occurs with other emotions after taking your remedy.

Homeopathic remedies work by raising your energy. When depressed, you usually also feel emotionally flat and physically lethargic. As your energy improves, motivation and enthusiasm spark again. You feel more sociable because you feel less disconnected from other people. You feel lighter emotionally, more engaged in your interactions with others, and when you regain your sense of humour you are able to have more fun.

Holly, a woman of 32, came to see me having suffered from depression for many years, in spite of twice-weekly therapy. 'I don't know why, but I can't really talk in therapy. It seems to reproduce the general situation in my life. I feel I don't have the tools inside myself to change things. I have lots of problems taking risks – because there's no sense of trust.' She felt fed up, sad and very closed off. It was difficult for her to open up about herself and her life. She would not tell friends how she was really feeling because she hated to be seen not to be coping. A close friend of hers had committed suicide, and she herself had recently broken up with her lover. She felt a deep depression and was no longer motivated by anything. Politics used to be extremely important to her, but she was no longer certain of their relevance.

'I was always miserable and terrified as a child. I was anxious about going blind, and I had to put on a light at night to reassure myself that I could really see.' She described her father as an aggressive, bullying character, and her mother as neurotic. 'I identify with my mother's anxiety. I always find something to worry about. I live in constant anxiety about "what if" something horrendous happens.' It had been difficult for her to cope with big changes, such as leaving home and moving to London. She spent too much time thinking about problems, which paralysed her. She was also a compulsive checker, which claimed much of her energy.

I started Holly's homeopathic treatment with the remedy Arsenicum album, because of her conscientious approach to her work and the compulsive checking – a clear sign that she distrusted her environment. The remedy reduced her depression to 'manageable levels' so that she was no longer feeling paralysed by it. She still felt uncertain about her future and woke early in the morning with a sensation of anxiety in her gut. Now when she woke early she just got up and got on with the day instead of lying in bed worrying about why she was not sleeping well. She still tended to keep the house overly tidy as a way of keeping other anxieties under control – which often seems to be a form of displaced activity.

A repeat of the Arsenicum further improved Holly's depression. What happened as the depression lifted was interesting and pointed the way to a subsequent remedy which was even more deeply effective than the Arsenicum – Natrum muriaticum.

Holly became more aware that psychotherapy was not helping her and got angry that she was not able to trust her therapist. This was a good sign, because it showed that her energy was mobilizing, and in a way that was far less self-destructive than when she was in a severely depressive state of mind. Usually Holly internalized anger, which just made her feel powerless and defeated. Now her anger was providing a useful kick-start for change. As the remedy started releasing her blocked energy, she became more aware just how much anger she was holding inside.

At this point I gave her the Natrum muriaticum, which corresponds to the pattern of behaviour caused by distrust and a deep isolation from early childhood. After taking it, Holly's energy levels increased and she was able to stay up late, giving her more time for herself. She experienced momentary panics as she felt an unfamiliar mood of psychological freedom. She also felt some degree of anxiety about no longer being depressed, because it had become such a familiar way of being. Natural breaks in her therapy appointments allowed her to feel less angry at the therapist and to start valuing the sessions, which were providing a forum for her to articulate what she did and did not want in her life. She was trying to assume less responsibility at work than before, where she managed a hostel for homeless people. In an attempt to control the stress at work and deal with underlying feelings of inadequacy, she had previously been excessively conscientious. Managing a busy hostel on her own had been too demanding, and she was taking too much mental responsibility for the problems there.

Holly moved into a flat share with someone else, which was the first time in a while that she had lived with another person, and her need compulsively to check gas, electricity and locks reduced greatly. Soon after, she finished psychotherapy and began a new relationship, a sign that she was ready to risk trusting someone emotionally.

The relationship was challenging, but Holly managed to hang on even after she discovered that her partner had seen someone else behind her back. She was angry and tearful but no longer reacted with anxiety or depression. As a result of her homeopathic treatment, Holly felt a lot more secure about her ability to make choices and to survive whatever the future might hold.

Like other people recovering from depression, she described a feeling of a void once her habitual worrying had gone away. The worrying had obviously been covering over a sense of need in her, an emptiness that could only begin to be filled in a healthy way once she acknowledged it for what it was. Her confidence gradually improved, and Holly started studying for a social work qualification.

Aurum metallicum	indicated for deep depression after the death or loss of someone much loved
China officinalis	used for people who are moody, alternating between depression and excitability. They are extremely touchy, taking offence at harmless comments.
Cimicifuga	used for people who feel as if they are under a heavy back cloud. It may help post-natal or pre-menstrual depression, as it is a good remedy for a range of gynaeco-logical problems.
Ignatia	used for depression which comes on as a result of grief after a loved one dies, or a partner leaves them
Lilium tigrinum	used for people who feel agitated internally, sometimes erupting in rage or dramatic emotional states, especially when they are upset by sexual issues in their relationship
Mercurius solubilis	used for people who become extremely withdrawn and introverted. Although they may feel intensely emotional inside they find it very difficult to express their feelings. Self-destructive impulses well up when they are in the depths of their despair.
Natrum sulphuricum	for depression in sensitive people who tend to listen to maudlin music. This remedy is particularly good if the depressive state starts after a head injury, and the sufferers also experience debilitating headaches as a result of the injury.
Pulsatilla	for people who suffer a great deal from loneliness and feel the need to be with people as much as possible. They feel easily hurt and spend a lot of time crying.
Sepia	helpful where a person feels defeated and depressed, and is literally worn out with cares

Soul Learning for Depression

If you are not feeling fulfilled and can't find meaning in your life, in order to rediscover your sense of purpose you need to consider what you must change in order to provide opportunities for fulfilment.

Disease

For many people, serious disease is their first or most frightening experience of the 'dark night of the soul'. During this confrontation with your mortality, you can be shaken loose from your moorings if the comfortable explanations you have constructed to explain the world to yourself collapse. Once you have accepted what has happened to you, this can also be an unexpected opportunity to change priorities and reframe your life.

Many people describe how the sharpened awareness of mortality that comes with illness prompts them to ask whether this is all there is. For many, it is a time to take stock in every area of life. Illness gives us clear premonitions of disintegration, which is a call for us to put our own personal house in order. Illness is very often telling you, through your body, that there is something wrong or out of balance in your life. Disease comes for a multitude of reasons, but in seeking to heal yourself you need to marshal all the resources at your disposal: physical, emotional, mental and spiritual.

By unleashing your blocked or damaged energy, you start to move the disease process in a curative direction, transforming physical pathology into less severe symptoms that indicate that your body is not functioning at an optimum level, before these are also rebalanced. Often, this is only possible where the disease has not been present for too long and where it is not too severe.

By the time you develop a disease, you may have been stuck in a dysfunctional energy pattern for some time. The pathology you have been diagnosed with is not a full explanation of why you have the symptoms you have, since many of them may date from earlier stages in the dis-ease process. Symptoms are usually the result rather than the cause of a stuck energy pattern, which means that early symptoms are often the direct result of what was happening in your life at the time.

The idea that pathology is behind the cause of all your problems underpins medical attempts to suppress conditions rather than get to their root cause. Suppression occurs when you try to wipe out a particular symptom rather than deal with it curatively, which would require treating it in a holistic context as one symptom among a range primarily caused by an imbalance in the energy body.

For instance, if you suffer from eczema, you may also become susceptible to asthma, another related allergic condition, as a result of using steroid creams to suppress the eczema. To treat eczema curatively, a homeopath needs to consider it along with all the other varied signs of imbalance in an individual's life before selecting a remedy that will act deeply to rebalance them.

Even when an illness strikes out of the blue, like a virus, the way we respond to it fits in with our own energy pattern. To find the constitutional remedy needed we can ask ourselves how we react to our illnesses. Homeopaths use the notion of susceptibility to explain why some people succumb to the harmful effects of bacteria and viruses, while others are seemingly unaffected. Viruses are all around us, but we can be made more vulnerable to their ill-effects through a prior state of dis-ease in our energy body. In dealing with illness, approaches that rebalance the energy body rather than merely treating the results of its imbalance will truly heal the person.

Mary had been diagnosed with gonorrhoea, a venereal disease, two days after the birth of her second child. She had caught it years previously, and now her son had a discharge in his eyes that tested positive to gonorrhoea. She did not have any symptoms of active gonorrhoea, but she did have a history of chronic gynaecological problems and ovulation pains. It looked as though her past of sex, drugs and rock and roll might be catching up with her in an unpleasant way. Although her lifestyle now was very healthy, the earlier years of neglecting the needs of her body had compromised the ability of her immune system to throw off infection effectively.

Mary had done very well in her professional life, but relationships were more difficult. She had had a good sexual relationship with a warm-hearted hedonist, but once children came along she became dissatisfied with his inability to function successfully in the outside world. She was the wage earner as well as the primary carer, yet her career had taken a nose-dive after she had had children.

I prescribed the homeopathic remedy Medorrhinum because of the gynaecological problems, which seemed to date from the bout of gonorrhoea she had had years ago, as well as lifestyle aspects of her case. This remedy can clear out residual sexually transmitted infections which still cause health problems although they are no longer active. Sure enough, the remedy produced an increased vaginal discharge for a few weeks, after which her gynaecological problems improved. She also said she felt 'brilliant' emotionally: she was much more confident and energetic than before. I also gave her son a few doses of the same remedy, which cleared up his eye problems.

I later followed her treatment with Thuja, another remedy associated with venereal diseases from the past and the long-term consequences they sometimes leave behind.

Anita developed a viral infection at the age of 15, which resulted in transverse myelitis, an inflammation of the spinal cord that causes paralysis of the affected nerves. She was hospitalized in intensive care for a month, and put on a ventilator. The ventilator tube damaged her windpipe, and because her healing mechanisms were overzealous she produced so much scar tissue that she lost the use of her voice.

Already an anxious person, Anita's anxiety levels became quite overwhelming when she suffered these problems after the myelitis. At the time of her illness, weight just dropped off her. She found it difficult to put on weight when she was depressed or anxious, while the tension in her throat had stopped her eating.

She always assumed the worst whenever she developed any symptoms and no longer had faith in her body's self-healing capacities: in fact, she always assumed her body would let her down. 'I feel very anxious since then, that something can just attack my body out of the blue. Every time I get ill I feel my body's out of control, and I imagine the worst.'

From being a clever and ambitious young woman, Anita had lost her confidence and became very depressed and withdrawn, crying almost constantly for the first three years after the infection.

She had more or less learned to live with an artificial windpipe and voice box, but another long-term effect of the neurological damage was an irritable, leaking bladder. Her lack of control over her bladder led to constant infections, which antibiotics relieved only for a short time. 'My bladder hasn't emptied properly for 10 years. And it seems to go into a spasm, spontaneously contracting and leaking. At the first urge, I need to go to the toilet straightaway. The neurologist gave me nerve sedatives which didn't help, and then suggested I use a catheter to empty my bladder. In the last year I've had at least seven bouts of cystitis, one of which went to my kidneys.'

As if all this were not enough to make her miserable, breathing through her neck had made Anita very vulnerable to chest infections. She felt lethargic and tired easily – more signs of a weakened immune system. Her glands were chronically swollen.

Anita's first homeopathic remedy, Causticum, triggered a lot of nerve activity: for a few days her arms and hands twitched. But within three days her chest felt a lot freer and her bladder became comfortable. She no longer had to get up at night to urinate, and urine stopped leaking out when she coughed or exercised. Her bladder control became at least 50 per cent better than prior to the remedy, in spite of the fact that such nerve damage is considered irreversible.

She reported that 'Homeopathy has brought back my power of concentration. For years I was like an obsessed person, hardly able to think about anything except how to manage my leaky bladder. I was constantly full of anxiety. Now the symptoms are so much better, but I don't even care if I wet myself. I feel much more confident.' Since starting homeopathic treatment, Anita has been feeling much more positive and energetic and much less tired. 'I'm a changed person. I feel properly supported for the first time, by my homeopath, and I have been able to overcome my fear and start living normally.'

Anita started to work again in the publishing industry. She said, 'I feel less ambitious than I did because I've got less need to prove myself. I am a creative person and I just want to be able to express that. I've accepted that my body was damaged by the illness and that I need to take more care of my body than others. If I need to lag behind what others are achieving, that's OK now.

'Homeopathy has helped with managing the symptoms resulting from the damage done by the virus: my spastic bladder, my breathing problems due to the artificial windpipe and my genetic predisposition to an overgrowth of scar tissue. It has saved me from endless rounds of antibiotics and further operations on my bladder, and has reduced my anxiety levels greatly.'

Shortly after starting a treatment to try to break down the scar tissue, Anita's friends commented that the scar on her neck looked less red and noticeable. The tincture, made from a plant called Thiosinaminum, can thin out keloids (an over-production of scar tissue) over a period of time. She decided to risk yet another operation to try and restore her windpipe, because there was much less risk of heavy scar tissue building up again. She was delighted to regain some vocal power, which is steadily improving.

Although Anita had been struck down out of the blue by a virus, the way in which she responded to the illness revealed the way her energy pattern was already shaped. The energy pattern of Causticum is shaped by a particular response to grief: in Anita's case, grief for her mother. Anita had always felt a sense of responsibility for her mother's happiness. As she entered adolescence, she had begun to feel guilty about her drives towards independence. The healing action of the remedy helped her to step into the independent life she had painstakingly created, so that she could fully enjoy it for the first time. She bought her own flat and started working on her problems in sustaining sexual relationships.

OTHER REMEDIES

Any of the many homeopathic remedies may be required, depending on the nature of the illness, along with the family history, metabolism and psychological profile of the individual. There are more than 3,000 remedies in use for treating various conditions.

Soul Lesson for Disease

Our soul needs us to manifest our purpose through our bodies. Try to honour your body as the vehicle of your soul.

Emptiness

Emptiness is the condition of feeling existence to be meaningless. This may be a projection of our inner state onto the world. It is really ourselves that feel empty. This feeling can make us hang on to regrets about the past and long for more of what we miss – even though the situation or person who assuaged our aloneness is no longer there.

Longing is an urge that often triggers the spiritual quest. This sense of longing can surface in any context. At root, the desire to merge is the soul's desire for connection with the universe. The crisis that abandonment plunges you into is a time for honouring your feelings of longing, whether for closeness, understanding or meaning, because longing impels you towards greater wholeness and fulfilment. In honouring that sense of longing, you honour your drive for meaning through connectedness. In order to plant the seeds of inner peace, you can explore the power of prayer or meditation.

Lee, a man of 45, said, 'I've spent years living in a community, with a partner, and bringing up children. Now suddenly I'm on my own. No one calls me – no one even answers my letters. For the first time in my life I'm having to deal with being alone.

'There was a comfortable safety in living in a community, but it didn't encourage me to live creatively. I prefer to be on the cutting edge, now. I realize that I've always been an outsider, and I need to recognize the positive aspect that role brings – that of bringing in new ideas and different ways of thinking and being.'

Lee was given the remedy Sulphur because of the way he had distracted himself from his deep sense of isolation with constant projects and a stream of bright ideas. Coming to terms with isolation involved letting go of the need to be with people just for the sake of it and recognizing that this basic need for company does not necessarily lead to fulfilling interactions.

In spite of his fears of being alone, Lee was able to delve into his feelings of emptiness, and out of that experience he found that he could begin to set up a spiritual practice. With the demands of others on him and his demands on others falling away, he developed more awareness of what was essential in his life. What he searched for was a real sense of union with the realm of spirit, rather than the surface togetherness of a community. He was searching for a life more congruent with the dictates of his soul.

Lee said, 'Being an outsider has attracted me to the mystical path – a spiritual path that has always attracted those on the margins of society. The way I see it, mystics have always been attracted to the experience of union with the divine – as outsiders that's something they are acutely aware of. Their outsider status allows them to find unorthodox paths to the divine.'

OTHER REMEDIES

Alumina	helps people who feel isolated as a result of the loss of their memory and other mental faculties. They feel confused and disoriented and are unable to make sense of their world. This is deeply distressing to them.
Anacardium	for people who feel alienated from the rest of society. They become hard and uncaring as a result of their isolation.
Carcinocin	indicated for people who feel like doormats and are always putting other people's needs first. Because they have no sense of themselves, they may end up feeling they have nothing more to give.
Cyclamen	used for people who feel depressed and anxious because of their feelings of dissatisfaction with life. They feel alone and hurt as a result of relationship problems.
Kali carbonica	for people who have paid more attention to the rules and structures in their lives, ignoring the content

| Platina | for people who feel superior and haughty as a defence against feeling how much they need contact with others |

Soul Lesson for Emptiness

You need to uncover a soul connection with yourself and others, through entering more deeply into your life.

Fatigue

Many of us suffer from unacceptable levels of tiredness as a result of a lifestyle in which far too many demands are made on us. Our whole physiology is geared up towards pushing ourselves, even though we might be 'running on empty' and do not know how to be idle. Our nervous system is kept on alert all the time, since the only means to get fuel in our depleted state is by keeping our nervous system keyed up, as if we are in a state of emergency. This is the kind of 'pit-stop fuel' that we get from drinking lots of coffee or eating food that is high in fats and sugars, which gives us a quick buzz of physical energy by raising our blood sugar.

This is very different from the kind of energy that flows from and within us when we are feeling a sense of well-being and are motivated to doing something because that is what we want to be doing. Feeling our pursuits are congruent with our heart's desires creates a reservoir of energy that feels abundant. We find that doing what we desire actually gives us more energy.

Many people who complain of fatigue and lethargy find that once they change their situations, for instance by changing a job that is not satisfying them, their energy improves immediately. They can get up earlier and yet feel more refreshed by sleep. They can pack a whole lot more activity into the day. For example, when you are taking a course that you find really interesting and inspiring, it suddenly becomes possible to fit in long hours of study and paid work as well as the domestic work of looking after yourself and others. You find you can do much more than you would have expected to be able to do.

Doing something that drains rather than boosts your energy and enthusiasm is probably the biggest factor in feeling excessively tired. Then there is the way you push past your immediate limitations, doing just one more thing before going to bed at night, cleaning up before you can get down to something else, rushing to get to the shops before they close, or carrying on working when you have got a feverish flu.

The habit of medicating a multitude of symptoms that tell you when you are pushing yourself too hard is also a problem. Examples of this misuse of medications include taking painkillers to mask the pain of tension headaches, antibiotics for the infections that become more frequent when we are feeling run down, and the use of steroids for a range of stress-related disorders such as eczema and asthma. As well as depleting your capacity for self-healing, the use of these drugs depletes your energy. Your symptoms are usually telling you to stop and make changes in your lifestyle, not to carry on and mask the problem by suppressing the symptoms with drugs. The indiscriminate use of drugs has left many people with dysfunctional immune systems and opportunistic health problems.

Alex, a young computer programmer, noticed that his energy levels were depleted after having suffered from glandular fever. Although there is no appropriate medication for glandular fever because it is a viral condition, his doctor gave him repeated courses of antibiotics to treat his sore throats. Not only did they not help, but they seemed to make him more tired. Instead of improving after a few months when the infection resolved itself, Alex continued to feel exhausted. He got worse, and eventually became so tired that he had to give up his job and move back to his parents' house because he could no longer look after himself. He had developed chronic fatigue syndrome. By the time I saw him he had not been able to work for several years and felt extremely depressed.

Alex had always prided himself on his good intellect and quick thinking. What disturbed him most was that he felt he could no longer think. It was a great effort for him just stringing the words together to make a sentence.

I gave him the homeopathic remedy Helleborus, because he felt that his brain had literally slowed down. He took much more time to make logical connections, and thoughts seemed to take longer to pass through the neurological wiring of his mind. He was frightened that he was unable to engage his brain in the way he used to, and he felt increasingly detached from the world.

Alex made a spectacular recovery after taking Helleborus. Over several weeks, his energy steadily increased and he regained his ability to concentrate and be alert. In a matter of months he was taking steps to get his life moving again and had signed up to do some further training at college. This was some years ago, and he has since gone from strength to strength.

OTHER REMEDIES

Cocculus — for people who are exhausted as a result of being deprived of sleep over a long period of time. They become nauseous, dizzy and disoriented.

Gelsemium — indicated where fatigue affects the muscles with tremendous weakness. People in this remedy pattern find it difficult to climb stairs or exert themselves: even their eyelids feel heavy and droopy. Any exertion causes a feeling of weakness and trembling.

Kali phosphoricum — a remedy for people who have gone through a long period of stress and have become worn out, mentally dull, and a bit nervous and over-sensitive with an easy startle reflex. They feel despondent and unable to cope with problems; they can't even watch the news on television because they get upset hearing about other people's misfortunes.

Muriatic acid — good for people who are weak with a raised temperature daily; they may need to sleep for many hours a day.

Picric acid — used for people who feel worn out after a period of intense intellectual activity. They become wiped out after studying for their final exams at college or university. They can no longer concentrate and become mentally slow.

Selenium — helpful for people who are so weak they can no longer make love with their partner. Their hair falls out and they feel much worse in the heat of the summer.

Silica	for people who feel tired after the slightest exertion. They have no stamina and they come down with lots of coughs and colds. The glands in their neck are chronically swollen as a result of all these infections.
Stannum	helpful for people suffering from tremendous weakness, who find it difficult even to hold a cup. They may feel particularly weak in the chest area.

Soul Learning for Fatigue

Try to stop doing and start being.

Fear

Nervousness and fearfulness are common because we recoil from experiences that are unknown or threaten our sense of self. Fear is the result of an energy pattern which is paralysed in a posture of fright. The person has taken up this stance in response to either a real or a perceived threat, which usually stems from earlier experiences in life but is sometimes the result of trauma to the mother during pregnancy. Fears and phobias can also result from shocking experiences in the past or from a slow erosion of the person's confidence. I have noticed that many women around middle age become more phobic and their lives more limited, because fear prevents them travelling or attempting anything new.

It is helpful to share your feelings of fear with other people. It is important to be honest rather than trying to deny these feelings or pretend they do not exist. We may feel ashamed of being seen not to be coping, but it is better to expose the fear so as to weaken its power over us. All our neurotic holding patterns are helped by sharing them with others.

In trying to overcome fear it can be helpful to take the risk of allowing yourself to experience the edge of what you feel comfortable with, that state where your anxiety makes you uncomfortable. Then you can try to learn to transform it. Fear is just a particular energetic pattern of responding to life, which can ultimately be transformed into intensely positive ways of responding.

Tim, a three-year-old boy, was brought to see me because he suffered from terrors in the night. He was unable to sleep in his own bed for any length of time. He could not sleep at all in the dark and screamed. He was very clingy with his mother, who was an actress and spent a lot of time working away while the children stayed with a nanny. His parents had split up shortly after the birth of Tim's younger brother, but they had never fully separated. Tim needed constant reassurance from his mother. He kept saying, 'I want you!', kissing, cuddling and climbing on her, and behaving in a babyish way, especially whenever his parents were together. This kind of regression to behaviour which is appropriate at a younger age is a common response to a sense of insecurity. It is a desire to return to the comforts that mothers give their children as babies.

Whenever Tim was upset, he cried desolately. Sometimes he seemed inconsolable. His mother said she felt he had a gaping hole inside him. He expressed it by complaining of always being hungry. He dreamed that people stole his food. He chewed his own clothes.

He was a very sensitive child and as a result of feeling so insecure he had developed eczema around his mouth. His insecurity stemmed from the breakdown of his parents' relationship. Their separation was uneasy, and their continued ambivalence about each other must have made him feel very uncertain about what to expect. I gave him the remedy Stramonium because he emanated the feeling that his very survival was threatened by the insecurity of his family situation. This remedy is needed when people become stuck in the energy pattern of terror.

The night after Tim first took the remedy he was especially unsettled and seemed very tearful, but within a few nights his sleep was much more peaceful. His parents took a long time to clarify their relationship, and were eventually reconciled. In the meantime they spent a couple of years having an unstable and, at times, volatile relationship. Periodically this insecurity got the better of Tim and his fear would overwhelm him again. At these times I would give him another dose of Stramonium. After each repeat dose he would sleep peacefully for another few months, although he still expressed his insecurity through a need for reassurance.

This was quite appropriate to his circumstances, and he only became more secure when his parents finally settled into a consistent and respectful way of relating to each other.

OTHER REMEDIES

Aconitum napellus	used to heal the fear of death when it comes on after a serious shock or a near-death experience
Belladonna	indicated where the person is phobic about dogs or other animals, and is very angry with the world as a result of their internal state of fear
Mancinella	helpful where there is fear of contamination or possession by insanity, evil, dark forces or the devil. I gave this remedy to one man who felt contaminated by his sexuality, which he experienced as dark and masochistic. He was tormented by the thought that he was not worthy of being on the spiritual path because his inner nature defiled him. These feelings precipitated psychotic episodes where he believed that he was involved in a battle with the forces of evil over his own soul. The remedy shifted him out of his psychotic state and enabled him to work on integrating the different facets of himself, which he did with the help of a psychotherapist.
Phosphorus	used for impressionable people with a vivid imagination who can't watch frightening films and who are fearful in the dark. They imagine that every creaking floorboard is evidence that a stranger is in the house. They may need to sleep with the light on.
Pulsatilla	for people whose fear is assuaged whenever people are around, whether they are close friends or just acquaintances. They can feel consumed by a fear of loneliness, of spending life alone, or of being alone in old age. It is difficult for them to spend any length of time on their own.

Soul Learning of Fear

To learn to trust others in order to feel safe in the world.

Feeling Trapped

This is the sensation you get when you feel too dependent, too weak to change your circumstances, or too bullied by others. You can also feel over-responsible: for instance when you are unable to shirk the duties of caring for an ageing relative or a dependent teenager.

Sometimes you feel trapped when the situation you are living in seems inflexible and you are saddled with burdensome responsibilities. It can be difficult to bear in mind that on some level you may have created this demanding situation yourself in order to learn and grow. Whether conscious or not, it can be helpful to consider that it is your soul's choice that you are living in this way. It is challenging to accept this notion with good grace, but it can help you to take some responsibility for your own participation in creating the situation. This helps you sharpen your appreciation of the present moment, rather than merely waiting passively for the future, or dwelling on the past.

You can look at your situation as a way of externalizing your inner sense of conflict. When you cannot decide what to do to change your circumstances, your inclination may be to blame other people who you feel have made you bend under a yoke. Fear of change can stop you from finding a way to ease your situation. Sometimes you would rather tolerate the difficulties you know than risk facing unknown problems. Alternatively, the fact that you do not know what your inner needs are may prevent you from finding ways to create space for them in your life, whether it be writing a journal or some poetry, nurturing friendships, or joining a support group with others in a similar situation.

Not identifying completely with the drama of the situation you find yourself in can help you to focus on the resources you do have. Thinking about the situation as an opportunity to learn something is helpful. The traditional idea of a yoke in the discipline of yoga is one of a dedication to a path of personal development.

This is also the idea behind the Islamic notion of submission, the belief that we have to submit to whatever our circumstances are in order to free our soul from an over-identification with the ego.

After Joan's third child was born by caesarian section, she had wanted to jump out of the hospital window. Medics call this 'post-partum psychosis', a syndrome where feelings such as rage, frustration and depression erupt because a woman feels totally out of control of her life after the birth of a baby.

Joan had brought up two sons on her own but had always had a need for time out. She often complained of feeling antisocial and wanting peace and quiet. She was very tired and weepy. She needed support but did not know how to get her needs met. She found it difficult to enjoy affectionate cuddles.

Joan felt deeply ambivalent about marriage and family life. She hated having a busy household to cook for and trying to deal with difficult teenage sons. She was always feeling tired and hated cleaning with a vengeance. At times she also hated her partner for not doing anything around the house. Instead of making her life easier, he just seemed to place more demands on her. She didn't feel that he considered them a team who needed to cope with this demanding situation together.

Joan's feelings of rage erupted just a few weeks after the birth, with crises in which she cried, screamed and threw plates at her husband, threatening him with knives. At 36, responsible for two teenagers and a new baby, Joan felt trapped. 'I need space. I need horizons. I want to go on holiday, with just my baby.'

The remedy Sepia (page 221) was indicated primarily because of Joan's unstable hormonal state after childbirth, which provided the ground for her feelings of resentment to erupt. Joan had already needed treatment in the winter of 1994 with the remedy Aurum metallicum because of her struggle with suicidal feelings. The winters were particularly hard on her because she suffered from seasonal affective disorder, a condition in which the lack of exposure to sunlight creates depression. A dose of Aurum metallicum (page 180) had lifted her depressive mood throughout the winter months, although she had needed to keep coming in for treatment occasionally when the stress of bringing up her sons had made her feel down again.

The Sepia granted Joan access to the sense of spaciousness in her soul, which allowed her internal freedom in spite of the limitations of her living situation. As a result, she was less resentful and more able to communicate her needs to her partner. She still seemed to be doing most of the housework, as her husband often failed to notice what needed doing. He'd spent years looking after no one's wishes but his own. Joan decided to stay together though, realizing that she did still want to be with him.

OTHER REMEDIES

Calcarea phosphorica	a good remedy for feelings of boredom and restlessness, especially in teenagers. These people desire to travel in order to change their environment temporarily.
China officinalis	for people who indulge in daydreams in which all their wishes are fulfilled
Conium	for those who become rigid in an attempt to cope with an inflexible situation
Drosera	indicated for people who respond to feeling trapped by becoming domineering towards other family members
Staphysagria	helpful for people who are tremendously frustrated about feeling unable to escape from a difficult situation. They may have fantasies based on a fictitious idea of romance as a means of being swept out of an unsatisfying domestic setup.
Zincum metallicum	used for people who are dissatisfied and are constantly complaining. Their restless feelings make them irritable and angry. Nervous overstimulation makes it difficult for them to concentrate, and they cannot apply their minds. They may feel confused, helpless and hopeless.

Soul Learning of Feeling Trapped

In order to find a sense of internal freedom, you need to learn not to identify with the drama of your situation. Instead, experiment with opening your eyes to your present situation and experiencing it fully. You may then get more out of it than you expect.

Forgiveness

Many of us hang on to unresolved emotions from hurtful or damaging experiences in the past. These feelings arise from unfinished business and can prevent us from getting on with life as it is in the present. Forgiveness is about freeing yourself from your connection to the past or to people who have hurt you through your wounding. Blame and vengeful thoughts can end up being ways of perpetuating your pain. Experiences of loss, abandonment, betrayal and abuse can leave you with hatred, anger or resentment towards the person responsible. Holding on to problems, resentment and frustration damages you because it creates body armouring, preventing the free flow of energy.

It may not be easy to get to a position where you can really let go of your attachment to the pain. You can't go back to life as it was before your betrayal, but you can move on.

One way through the unfinished business of the past is to understand your psychological pain in relation to those old experiences. Try to acknowledge your emotions and then move out of this – sometimes necessarily – self-centred perspective to a wider frame in which you can acknowledge the various ways in which all of us are damaged.

A lack of forgiveness maintains a negative connection with the person who has hurt us, and also blocks the exchange of energy between ourselves and others because our sense of safety or trust has been damaged. Forgiveness actually breaks the connection, and re-establishes the ability to interchange with others in the here and now. When you feel unforgiving you judge and blame others. When you judge others you separate yourself from them.

In order to forgive you can go into the emotional softness of compassion for yourself and your wounds, rather than into the hardness of having to remain defensive. You may need to love yourself first, or to forgive yourself before you can let go of the hurt or blame. Compassion can go on to convert your feelings of anger or hatred into mercy, which is when you allow yourself to comprehend the imperfections, inadequacies or damage in others.

Hannah had spent decades struggling with anorexia, from her early teens. She had always felt that her parents passed her over in favour of her brother, and she could never live up to their high standards. Her father worked in the field of overseas aid, and because they moved around every few years, Hannah had never learned how to form close relationships with others. As a teenager she felt insecure and unattractive, and when an early marriage ended in an acrimonious divorce, her anorexia took hold again. She dwindled away to almost nothing and had to be hospitalized on several occasions. Although her parents took her home and looked after her, Hannah blamed them for her predicament, and tried to establish a relationship with someone miles away at the other end of the country.

At the time she came to see me, Hannah had two failed marriages behind her and was still struggling with a poor body image. Although painfully thin, she hated the way she looked and spent hours every day working out in the gym. Hannah's obsessional attitudes meant that she tried to control everything: food, her appearance, her lifestyle and her relationships with others. She was rigid and rarely able to relax. Her punitive attitudes were a little more lenient towards others than towards herself, but her boyfriend, Neil, found her very controlling. She was very dependent on him, but needed everything to be on her own terms, otherwise she would get extremely anxious and fearful.

Hannah was desperate to maintain the relationship, but her desperation was pushing her partner away and she frequently found she couldn't eat. She had always been uncomfortable about eating in public, but she found that as her fear of the relationship breaking up increased, she was unable to eat in front of Neil. She had never been able to have an orgasm in her sexual relationships, because it was so difficult for her to let go of needing to be in control. She was plagued by cystitis and had suffered a lot of kidney infections as a result.

The remedy Arsenicum album reduced Hannah's anxiety, which enabled her to stop her habitual punitive and self-destructive behaviour before it made her seriously ill again. Although the remedy dramatically improved her psychological state, it was a long time before Hannah felt ready to contact her parents and attempt to repair their damaged relationship. Although she was still extremely sensitive to their demanding and manipulative attitudes, once she no longer felt fearful that she might succumb to anorexia she managed to achieve the emotional distance to see them as separate. She realized that they were elderly now, and no longer had the power over her that they had had when she was a child. As the homeopathic treatment helped her feel less desperate and needy within herself, and she got more support from her relationship, Hannah was able to free herself of her anorexic obsessions.

OTHER REMEDIES

Anacardium	can open people up to the possibility of forgiveness when they feel incarcerated in their defensive armouring
Aurum metallicum	can heal the deep grief in people who have become heavily depressed as a result of earlier betrayals
Natrum muriaticum	for those who feel resentful about old misunderstandings. They feel particularly let down or betrayed when intimate relationships end. This remedy helps them let go of stuck emotions and respond more appropriately to their feelings about the current situation. A useful distinction is that feelings arise as a result of what's happening in the present moment, while emotions are usually to do with past situations.
Nitric acid	used for those who feel misanthropic, interacting with others in a critical, aggressive and hostile manner. They are pessimistic, and vindictive towards those who have hurt them.

Soul Learning of Forgiveness

You need to let go of your attachment to fear and blame and to be fully present in the moment, rather than defended against past hurts. To move towards forgiveness, foster compassion for yourself and others.

Guilt

Guilt is essentially about your relationship to other people; when you feel guilty it is because you think that you have transgressed an ethical boundary. You may have internalized the moral code of your family or society, or you may have developed your own code through the course of your life experiences. Sometimes you may be internalizing the guilt of others, which needs to be put right back where it belongs.

In some ways, guilt can contribute to your maturity through a sense of taking responsibility for your life. It can actually serve a useful function when it acts as a curb on your narcissistic desires: without it you might behave selfishly, without any thought of the consequences for yourself and others. As you mature, it can serve to remind you of your responsibilities towards other people and refines your evolving sense of integrity.

In its negative aspect, guilt is often connected with a perfectionist attitude towards oneself and others, in which you are not allowed to make mistakes. The Catholic tradition of guilt regards it as an atonement for our misdeeds. The problem is that guilt rarely expiates your sense of wrongdoing. Instead it stays lodged in the psyche, eroding your sense of self-worth. It can produce low self-esteem and makes the sufferer feel unworthy. It can erupt into a crisis of conscience, where you doubt the veracity of what you're doing.

Guilt can become narcissistic when you use it as an excuse to carry on obsessing about yourself rather than admitting any mistakes you have made and then taking responsibility for making changes. It can be a refusal to admit your weaknesses and imperfections – in other words that you are human and flawed like everyone else. This kind of guilt is associated with shame about not living up to other people's expectations. Shame is connected with feeling exposed or flouting public mores. Healing shame involves forgiving ourselves. In forgiving ourselves, we extend to ourselves the sense of compassion that we feel more easily for other people.

Guilt is an internalization of shame in which you feel you have not lived up to the ideals implicit in your own code of honour. Guilt alerts you to where you have transgressed boundaries and affronted your own sense of integrity. The first step to healing guilt is to share your imperfection. Be honest about your mistakes rather than denying them or pretending they do not exist. It is usually shame that makes us try to cover things up, but it is better to expose whatever you feel guilty about because it then loses some of its power. If you hold back, you overidentify with the thing you are trying to keep secret. Letting go of resistance frees you from the habitual incarcerations of the mind.

In letting go of introspective and secretive tendencies you are learning to open up to and trust others again. If you have consciously harmed someone, guilt can help you move from a state of remorse to one of reparation, where you re-establish your connection and pave the way for forgiveness. Being humble and expressing your regret enables you to move out of your stance of withdrawal and reconnect with others.

Another way of looking at it is that it takes courage not to suppress those aspects of yourself that don't fit in with your self-image and world view. The radical psychiatrist R. D. Laing argued that true guilt is the product of not fulfilling your obligation to yourself to realize your true potential and be yourself. Healing guilt involves taking the risk of reconnecting with your deeper sense of self.

Ben was dogged by a physical condition which he felt was a sign of a betrayal of his marriage. As a result of a one-night stand he had picked up herpes, and he felt contaminated by the experience, as if the herpes was a physical stigma. Infidelity had left an obvious mark on him, and he felt deeply ashamed and inhibited in his sexuality.

The experience burned in his consciousness because it was like a shameful secret he carried everywhere, which created such intense guilt that he was in a constant state of anxiety. Although it was irrational, he was afraid of being exposed. The anxiety was so intense that he could not concentrate on his work or on looking after his family. He felt that he literally could not think, nor could he take in any information because his mind was constantly preoccupied with his internal state. He suffered from constant severe headaches as a result of all this self-induced stress.

Ben's path to healing started with the age-old ritual of confession. The homeopathic consultation provided an opportunity to confess his indiscretion to a stranger, without any negative repercussions. Just sharing a secret means you feel less alone with it. When it is received by someone else in a non-judgemental way, you are more able to allow yourself to accept your mistake.

I prescribed Thuja for Ben's particular energy pattern, which was stuck in a stance of hiding. He felt he had betrayed his partner, but the deeper reason he was so upset was that he had betrayed himself first, since he had not behaved in a way that was congruent with his values.

Thuja resolves an inner state of conflict where people feel rotten and try to hide those aspects of themselves which they consider too unpleasant to reveal. They feel that others would not like them if they knew their true character. This attempt to hide their 'shadow side' closes people down emotionally, and they become secretive and sometimes even deceptive in an attempt to cover up.

The remedy began to clear Ben's mind, and he found that he could complete daily tasks, although the headaches were initially still too crippling for him to be able to concentrate well at work. The fact that he could not just get on with his life straightaway after taking the remedy made him feel anxious and panicky, but he needed to accept his past mistake fully and forgive himself before he could finally heal the shame that was the cause of his neurosis.

Feelings of shame around sexuality are endemic, because as a culture we are deeply uncomfortable with sex. When growing up we are often made to feel ashamed of our emerging sexuality and attempt to repress it. In healing this kind of shame, we need to accept our own nature as sensual, sexual beings.

OTHER REMEDIES

Anacardium	used for people who humiliate others because of their own feelings of worthlessness
Chelidonium	for people who have been domineering towards others, coercing others into accommodating their wishes. People needing this remedy have trouble with their liver or gall-bladder.
Digitalis	for people with an erratic heart rate and slow pulse, who feel guilty because of affairs of the heart, feeling they have not behaved well

preparing for soul work

Kali bromatum	for people who worry that they are being punished by God as a result of their mistakes
Leuticum	indicated where people feel contaminated, and wash their hands obsessively as a result
Natrum muriaticum	helps people to stop brooding over past mistakes in intimate relationships. They are over-sensitive to perceived criticism and they tend not to express their emotions at the time. This attitude means that misunderstandings can accumulate.

Soul Lesson of Guilt

Developing congruence between the inner and outer you involves identifying with the essential truth of your own being, in order to manifest that.

Hypersensitivity

An energy body that is depleted or fragmented can give rise to tremendous hypersensitivity, which is a condition of being literally at odds with our environment. Allergy means 'altered reaction' – hay fever, for example, is one of a range of hypersensitive reactions to normally harmless substances. Allergies such as hay fever and asthma are currently at epidemic proportions, which shows that we are living in a way that is out of balance with our environment. Our immune systems identify common substances which should be innocuous as harmful and then react defensively. This is the body's way of trying to maintain its physical integrity in the face of an ecosystem that has been polluted. Our environment is full of toxic chemicals and our foodstuffs are being manipulated for commercial ends, without thought to how we can digest and process such devitalized and damaged substances.

Any assault on the body, through chemicals, drugs or psychic shock, can create hypersensitivity in an individual. Once this develops, you become more sensitive to drugs and chemicals, which de-stabilize you further.

Kate was housebound and rarely able to leave her London flat for more than a few minutes at a time. She was so weak that she had to use a wheelchair to go outside. She could hardly cope with going out at all because of the sensory overload of just being on the street. Noises were too loud, movement too intense, colours too vivid. Kate even had to wear sunglasses indoors or else stay still in a darkened room. She complained that she got bored, but, if she moved, she felt as if her head was in a roller coaster, and the tension in her spinal chord radiated throughout her body.

Kate described her body as feeling 'scattered', as if it were in bits. She was sometimes troubled by a strange sensation that her body did not really exist at all. She needed to concentrate all the time on holding herself together if she was to feel anything approaching normality. She described her brain as confused. Talking on the phone aggravated how she felt, because when she was distracted she felt disoriented and more spaced out. Sometimes she felt as if she were leaving her body.

By the age of 10, Kate had lost her family, home and friends. Her father had died, and from that time on she felt that she had no psychic protection. She had been her father's favourite; after his death the family had moved house. She told me that she had never got on with her mother, who remarried soon after.

Kate described herself as taking refuge in a false state of being. After her own marriage ended in her twenties, she had had a breakdown and started living alone. Kate cried a lot when she was on her own, but tried to reassure herself by reassuring others: she carried on smiling and being friendly in spite of feeling tense and frightened inside. She hated being alone but was unable to tolerate more than one person inside her house. She hated crowds and was fearful about dying; she developed panic attacks during which she felt she was dying.

After I gave her the remedy Cannabis indica, Kate experienced much more vitality. Her nervous system became more relaxed and the muscle spasms she had suffered from were reduced by half within the first month. Her mind became sharper and clearer, but with this she noticed a lot of anxieties resurfacing. Her heart would race and she was apprehensive about meeting certain people when she was out in her wheelchair. The anxiety was a sign of her greater vitality and the challenges brought about by her newfound ability to get out and about in the world.

Kate's fearfulness gradually diminished as the energy that she previously spent on constantly monitoring her own state was directed more externally. This constant preoccupation with the minutiae of her pains and sensations had exacerbated her hypersensitivity; as the remedy worked, she quickly felt better. Without having to pay so much attention to where her body felt pained and blocked, Kate's energy could flow into other areas, releasing the tight energy knots created by both her physical symptoms and her psychological responses. The block of fearfulness began to dissolve into a greater trust in the world, which she described as a return to her original childhood state. On a psychological level, this meant letting go of the attitude that the world was a hostile place, transforming a self-centred neurosis to a recognition of interconnectedness.

Kate's path to cure involved healing the separations and losses she had found so difficult in childhood because of her sensitivity and fragility.

OTHER REMEDIES

Arsenicum album	for people who feel weak and prostrate but are also extremely sensitive to anything being out of place in their environment. They are driven to tidy things even though they feel completely exhausted or overloaded.
Asarum	good for people whose nerves are oversensitive and feel at a pitch. The slightest noise seems to penetrate their bodies.
China officinalis	for people who feel sensitive and touchy and take offence easily. Their skin feels so hypersensitive that they can only wear soft, natural fabrics. These people are very imaginative and live in a world of fantasies: they are constantly making plans and daydreaming.
Coffea	indicated for those who are sensitive to coffee and become hyped up and overstimulated, with a rapid heart rate. People in this remedy pattern are often insomniacs; their minds are continually buzzing with thoughts which are both excited and anxious.
Ignatia	for people who suffer from emotional oversensitivity. They have high expectations of others and constantly feel disappointed.

Phosphorus	helpful for people who are very sensitive to atmosphere. People in this remedy pattern will take on other people's moods or symptoms. For instance, if they are expecting a friend who suffers from migraines, they get a headache while waiting for them.
Sulphuric acid	helpful for people who are allergic to exhaust fumes and who are hypersensitive to chemicals. They may feel hurried and stressed, and they are easily overstimulated by toxins.
Theridion	indicated for people who suffer from extreme sensitivity to noise, which sets their teeth on edge. They feel sick, anxious and sleepless when overwhelmed by things, and often feel panicky.

Soul Lesson of Hypersensitivity

Find harmonious ways to live that are more in balance with the natural world.

Internal Conflict

Internal conflict occurs when different aspects of yourself want to engage with life in different ways. You need to move forward, but you're aware that what happens in the future is shaped by current priorities. The choices you make now will have effects that ripple on. This awareness is central to taking responsibility for yourself and others. It takes courage to step into the unknown when so much is at stake. You may be unable to make a choice, even when the options may seem very clear. You are sitting on the fence, which is an uncomfortable place to be. When you consciously know which way you should be going but feel unable to move, you lose impetus by berating yourself. But as soon as you are about to take a resolute step, indecision rears up and freezes your foot in mid-air.

Whenever you are feeling ambivalent, there is some kind of internal mechanism going on that allows you to distance yourself from whatever is happening in your life. You need to ask yourself whether this mechanism exists because you are doing something that you shouldn't be doing, or because you aren't doing something that you should be doing.

On the soul level, all the choices we make are significant. On the one hand there is no such thing as a right or wrong path, because all paths lead to our ultimate destination, whatever that is. On the other, there is a right or wrong way to go about things. Our path in life is never clearly signposted, and we do not have the wisdom to know our ultimate destination. The path that seems obvious may not be the one we should be on, while the other, less inspiring path might actually have more integrity. Moral rather than spiritual certainties can help us take a step forward, and we can leave the rest up to our soul.

This is why spiritual teachings counsel abandoning notions of personal will in favour of going with the flow, a strategy which leaves it up to the realm of the spirit to determine the challenges we need in our lives.

Nicole, a married woman in her early forties, scandalized her synagogue community by falling in love with a much younger man. For a long time she felt that they were soul mates, and she longed to leave her partner to be with him. However, she was aware that he was at a different stage in his life and would want to go on and have children, while she already had four. The months stretched into years as she felt torn in two, equally unable to trust the relationship or to let go fully.

She came to me at various points in a state of longing and grief, unable to jeopardize the life of her family in order to follow the dictates of her heart. I gave her the remedy Pulsatilla, which pulled her out of her immediate state of dejection.

Finally, Nicole decided that she should let go of the young man and stay with her partner, in spite of the difficulties they had in communicating. Their children were becoming more and more distressed by any sign that the two of them were not getting along, and she knew it would be very difficult for them should she decide to make a relationship with the young man in the face of so much social disapproval. She made her decision more for her children than for herself, and it was hard on her.

Nicole took the difficult decision to stay in a problematic relationship and work at it. She and her partner began couples' counselling, re-learning vital communication skills. They also sought professional help for guidance concerning some challenging aspects of parenting.

The Pulsatilla helped Nicole to begin to heal her grief and accept how much her personal history had predisposed her to dissatisfaction, resentment and anger. Her difficult relationship with her father, who had married a woman half his age after her mother died when Nicole was in her twenties, was clearly mirrored by her own situation. 'My father wouldn't come to visit me after he remarried, and I felt as if I was never wanted by him.'

Her path to healing involved contacting her estranged father in order to mend the rift. She realized that she had harboured a lot of anger towards men, along with a belief that men were useless. In her more dismissive moments, that was how she saw her partner. Once she realized that she was loading her relationship with feelings that were not necessarily appropriate to it, she was able to start clearing them.

OTHER REMEDIES

Anacardium	for people who feel like a square peg stuck in a round hole: whichever way they turn, nothing feels comfortable
Baryta carbonica	indicated for people who lack the confidence to take a step, even if they think they know what they should be doing
Graphites	helps people who can't get their mind around the issues that need to be analysed in order to come to a decision. They feel dull and are hampered by a slow metabolism
Silica	helps those who have convictions but lack the confidence to express them in a public setting
Thuja	helps people who feel tortured by a secret. This paralyses them. The remedy helps them accept and integrate aspects of themselves which they see as failings.

Soul Learning of Internal Conflict

Deal with ambivalence by engaging more fully with your life. Consider the idea that whatever happens to you in life, you will learn from it.

Jealousy

Jealousy occurs when you feel threatened by loss, especially when the attention of the person you desire is directed elsewhere, rather than toward you. If you notice, or imagine, that someone you love is more interested in someone else, you feel inadequate by comparison. You may or may not express your emotions, but if you make a scene, it's in an attempt to reclaim attention, by whatever means. When you feel jealous of someone else, you may be envious about whatever they have that seems so much better than what you have. Women stuck in the energy pattern of Lachesis often manifest this envy towards other women. On some level they want to step into the other woman's place, desiring whatever success this woman seems to have, be it with status, looks or lovers.

When jealousy takes the form of sexual possessiveness, you implicitly minimize your own sexual magnetism in assuming that others may be more attractive to your mate. Jealousy is often about insecurity in a relationship, especially sexual insecurity. This insecurity can be rooted in a fear of your own power, and especially of your sexual power. You may feel your sexuality is not powerful because you haven't fully inhabited it and you're not always comfortable with feeling sexual or sensual. But if you have problems with jealousy, you are more likely to have a strong sex drive that needs to be expressed according to the dictates of your heart, and met with equal passion.

In contemporary culture, our self-image rarely encompasses a whole, healthy sexuality. Many of us split off our sexuality, sometimes denying it altogether, sometimes expressing it in partial or distorted ways. Underlying our negative emotional reactions is a fear of sexuality and a judgement about it. Healing jealousy involves accepting ourselves as sexual beings, and allowing ourselves to enjoy our sensual nature.

Susan came to see me because of acne rosacea, an inflammatory skin condition affecting her face. The condition had started after she had attempted being lovers with a long-term woman friend, which had not worked because their relationship had become rather competitive. The other woman, Brigid, was popular and gregarious, and Susan had always felt as if she were marginalized in the relationship. She would get needy and demanding in a childlike way, crying and throwing tantrums. Her partner had tried to be sympathetic but did not have the time to devote to Susan. They were able to resume their friendship after their sexual relationship ended, but Susan still noticed her own feelings of envy and competition. Although they were no longer lovers, she wanted to be special to Brigid.

Part of this was about needing really to accept and own her own personal power. Susan worked in an environment where it was not always acceptable to be ambitious and go-getting. She felt this at odds with her spiritual path, which encouraged a new-age, sensitive model of femininity. She was a very competent and able person, extremely effective at seeing projects through and working at a high level in the world of commerce. She needed to accept this side of herself and allow others to see her as the powerhouse that she was.

Because she didn't like having an unsightly skin condition which people reacted to badly, Susan had developed issues about contamination. For instance she was quite hypochondriacal about the possibility of catching other people's illnesses. In a way, this could be seen as a lack of faith in her own physical integrity, in spite of the fact that she was conscientious about taking good care of her health. This was another manifestation of her belief that others could influence her, regardless of her own efforts.

When Susan gave in to her jealous moods, she felt competitive and lost touch with her warm, loving nature. Because of her workaholism, she was often hard and unloving to herself. She tended to cut off her sexual feelings in relationships whenever things became too difficult. She experienced any form of emotional withdrawal as emotional abandonment and responded by becoming cool herself.

In reality, however, her emotions were strong, and she would often spend sleepless nights crying and going over real or imagined problems in a relationship. Lachesis was instrumental in reconnecting Susan's heart and soul. She became able to celebrate her friendships and intimate relationships and remain open and loving, even when she felt her own need for a close sexual relationship was unfulfilled.

Apis	for people who are protective and controlling, jealously protecting their family unit
Hyosycamus	indicated where the person has an exhibitionist and provocative sexuality, coupled with suspicion of others
Lilium tigrinum	indicated where there is conflict between a strong sexuality and a repressive morality, such as traditional religious values
Tarentula hispanica	healing for spiteful, vindictive jealousy
Veratrum album	used when the person feels superior and puts on airs

Soul Learning for Jealousy

Experience love as a spiritual energy that you can access at any time, rather than as something to be invested in another person. Learn that love is an energy flow that is not dependent on an object for its existence.

Loneliness

Loneliness is a major problem in Western society, as a result of the difficulties many of us have in getting close to others and sustaining intimate relationships. Instead, our lifestyle offers endless activities in pursuit of pleasure – from clubbing to the movies – but they distract only momentarily from a sense of isolation. Alienation stems from a lack of connection with others, and leaves you feeling separate even in company. You can suffer from inner loneliness whether your life is full and busy or seemingly empty.

You feel ultimately alone whenever you close your heart to yourself. This can happen when you internalize a belief that others will judge your mistakes: for instance, when a woman facing a pregnancy termination feels unable to talk to anyone about it, not even close friends.

Sometimes you develop an independent, strong and defiant awareness of your individuality as a result of dealing with challenging situations in life.

While this persona is great as a survival strategy and helps you get on in life, it can create a self-sufficiency that makes it difficult to reach out for help. If you prefer to deal with problems on your own, it can be hard to admit to being vulnerable, because you regard it as a sign of weakness.

We tend to look for affirmation of who we are from other people, such as our families, friends, lovers or companions. They help us build an identity. If you do not feel validated by others or have no companions to mirror you back to yourself, you can feel totally isolated. Yet, what is mirrored back by friends and acquaintances is not necessarily who we are – it may just be the habitual responses we have accumulated as a result of the strategies we have devised for getting through life experiences. Your personality is not the essential core of you. Your core is something intangible and indefinable, which may become perfectly clear to yourself and others as you develop through your life journey. When you are permeated with inner wisdom it radiates out like a shining beacon of light, just as a baby is a radiant being, taking everything in and giving out in an open and receptive way. A baby's sense of identity is not in his or her personality or appearance, but in his or her responses to all the new experiences life is giving them.

Sarah, a woman in her thirties, had survived cancer yet she could not allow herself to celebrate her recovery. She wept rivers of tears, saying she was grieving for her lost self. 'I'm consumed by the sense of everything I haven't done yet, and everything I didn't have. I always thought of myself as having a happy childhood; now I realize that it was actually like being in a desert. Our existence was small and mean and boring – nothing ever happened, and it still feels as if nothing is happening in my life.'

Sarah was tormented by a fear of being left alone, although she had always been a loner. She lived on her own and saw very few friends. She habitually curbed her emotions and rarely exposed herself. She had always been unable to express any angry feelings, because she was afraid that her anger would be unacceptable to others. She tended to remove herself from difficult situations rather than confront them. It was as if she had a fear of really engaging with people, although inside she felt almost desperate with loneliness.

Her father had asked her to look after her mother just before he died, and Sarah felt guilty that her mother now needed to go into care. Her mother was deteriorating mentally and did not seem to recall that her husband was dead. She insisted that Sarah's father was about to come home and talked about him all the time, which Sarah found very upsetting. She still had not come to terms with his death herself.

At times she felt the presence of her father, which terrified her. She always slept with the light on to ward off ghosts. She felt that her father knew all her secret thoughts. 'I am haunted by my father because of a secret I've kept from my family. I had a termination once when I got pregnant after a night of casual sex. But if I had known that I wouldn't be in a relationship by this age, and that I might not have another opportunity, I would have had the baby. I regret not having had a child because I don't believe I'll ever have another chance.'

Sarah's breast cancer developed just two months after her father's death. She said, 'I feel it has something to do with my sexuality. I find it difficult to connect properly. I don't know how to have relationships. I feel I missed out on a stage in my development. My parents kept me childish, and my father could never cope with my anger.'

I gave her the remedy Pulsatilla, because of the intense neediness that underlay her sense of isolation. This remedy is often indicated for people who surround themselves with others because they hate to be alone, but Sarah was unable to do so because fundamentally she didn't accept herself. She felt guilty about her past decision about the pregnancy and the choices she was forced to make about her mother, because she felt that she wasn't able to keep the promise she had made to her father.

The remedy enabled her to heal the hurt and the deep need that arose out of her aborted chance to be a mother, while helping her heal the mothering relationship she had been forced to assume with her own mother. Sarah did move her mother into a home, which involved selling both her mother's house and her own so that she could live closer to the nursing home. Effecting these changes in her life got her out of her loneliness, and eventually she was able to start addressing her desire for friendship and love.

Aurum metallicum	for people with an intense and idealistic character who feel devastated by the loss of a family member or a broken relationship
Cyclamen	for those who feel depressed, weepy and isolated
Hura	indicated where there is a tremendous sense of abandonment, and the person feels ostracized by those around him or her
Psorinum	indicated for people in pessimistic and despairing states. They are anxious that they might end up destitute or homeless.
Stramonium	helps people who are very fearful as a result of feeling totally alone

Soul Learning of Loneliness

Learn that you are never alone, because, on a soul level, you are always connected to others. You need to find strength and support within your being and develop a feeling of connectedness. Knowing that we are all going through the same struggle can help you to feel your humanity and to realize that you are not alone.

Loss and Grief

Whether you suffer from the loss of a pet, a job, a home, or a loved one, you may have trouble letting go. You find it difficult to accept that death is final or that the person you love has left for good.

However irrational it is to do so, you may experience loss as abandonment. The end of a relationship feels like a mini-death, and you are shocked, wounded or betrayed if the person you have been involved with leaves of their own volition. Abandoned by the object of your love, you risk losing access to your own loving feelings. You no longer feel connected to the world through the one you love, and you feel isolated and alone.

Many of us become emotionally crippled by such experiences of loss. Sometimes we are crippled because we let these feelings get in the way of our current attachments and we withdraw from life. Grief and loss produce an armouring around the heart which initially seems protective, but which does not really protect you: in fact, it usually prevents you from feeling any kind of love, so that you get more and more armoured against the possibility of opening your heart again.

As a society, our idea of romantic love is fuelled by the dream of unconditional love. It always eludes us, because this kind of love rarely exists on the human level. If you have invested your hopes and longings in a particular person, they will be dashed when that person leaves. You are left in a dishevelled heap, carrying the energetic pattern of grief and abandonment.

Author Stephen Levine describes grief as unfinished business. He says we often feel a sense of loss due to the awareness that we could have had so much more with a person. The experiences we shared with that person were somehow not intense enough, and we did not connect on a deep level. There was a regret that we could not fully allow that person to get close, or that we needed more.

This increases the sense of separation and ultimate aloneness. A feeling of emptiness makes you hang on to regrets about the past, and you are stuck with longing for more, even though the other person is no longer there. The challenge of loss is to try and trust in the greater wisdom of the universe, for we cannot always understand why we are forced to let go of people and situations we love and are forced to move on. Finding the courage to let go, we can experience the pleasures of making new connections, building new relationships and opening to love again.

Theresa, a woman in her thirties, saw me for treatment for the painful rheumatoid arthritis she had suffered from throughout her life. After we had talked at length, it seemed to both of us that it was related to a suppression of painful emotions. It was very much connected with psychological pain and had worsened after shocks and traumas in her life.

A boyfriend had committed suicide some years earlier, and Theresa still felt shocked and guilty because she had not realized at the time how desperate he had been. She was sad and depressed, and although she rarely talked about it or cried, she spent a lot of time brooding about what had happened.

I hardly knew whether Theresa currently had a relationship or not, because she did not respond to my queries. Eventually she mentioned that she had had a relationship with a married man for a few years. It seemed to me as if she had internalized the enforced habit of secrecy that the relationship entailed.

There was a deeper underlying emotional trauma in her life, however. Theresa had never met her father, and, when she finally found the courage to make contact with him, he responded as if he did not want to know anything about her existence. This reaction wounded her, but she could not let go of the hankering to get to know him.

The homeopathic remedy Natrum muriaticum helped Theresa build up the confidence to face the rejection that she feared, and she made a trip to Denmark to visit her father. Although he was unable to be welcoming, she handled this second attempt to create a bridge in a different way. The first time she had been devastated and had felt wounded for several years. This was what happened without the help of homeopathy. The second time, she had already taken the remedy and it had healed some of her deep feelings of grief. Natrum muriaticum cleared old feelings of pain, abandonment and mistrust enough to allow the desire to meet her father to resurface. Even though he clearly could not handle her reappearance in his life, at a deep level Theresa was partially healed by the simple fact of their contact. In some way just the fact of their meeting affirmed her existence. It was like a jigsaw piece falling into place inside her, which allowed her to feel more whole. In my own experience, this 'fitting into place' allows you to form relationships with those who are more amenable to making a commitment.

OTHER REMEDIES

Aurum metallicum	indicated where suicidal feelings develop after a prolonged period of grieving. The person suffers deep feelings of despair and does not want to live.
Ignatia	corresponds to a numb condition, such as the state of shock that develops straight after the death or loss of someone close. During shock there is a physical seizing up as well: people in shock feel they cannot breathe

preparing for soul work

deeply or swallow properly. They may have the feeling of a lump in the throat, which is associated with unexpressed tears, and they feel better after a good cry. Their sense of dashed dreams or disappointed love creates a feeling of hopelessness.

Natrum carbonicum good for people who have a gentle and self-sacrificing disposition, which makes them accommodating, but who can harbour resentment if someone has hurt them. Because of their emotionally sensitive nature, they feel the loss of people intensely. However, it is difficult for them to express sadness; they seem unaffected or jokey on the surface but are sensitive to emotionally moving music.

Natrum muriaticum used for the deep sense of loss that comes after you lose a partner of many years or a child. People in this remedy pattern experience a livid, searing pain that is so deep it cannot easily be spoken about, and it preoccupies them for much of the time. Their experience may leave a numbness on the emotional level, where they feel that part of them has died with their loved one. They may become bitter and resentful at the experiences life has dealt them.

Soul Learning of Loss and Grief

Coming to terms with loss involves resolving to live more fully in each and every moment, rather than hanging on to the incomplete past or shielding yourself against the present.

Low Self-esteem

Self-esteem is very much linked to feelings of connection with and acceptance by others. When we experience our common humanity, we feel closer to and more caring towards others, and we feel that they appreciate us. When we feel isolated or alienated, our sense of self is undermined and we may suffer from a sense of worthlessness. Lack of self-esteem can be produced by undermining experiences in childhood, when we are perhaps made to feel that love and approval are conditional upon our fulfilling the expectations of others. Too much criticism can undermine our precarious sense of self when we are growing up.

Low self-esteem is endemic in a society that pays lip service to the importance of the individual, yet is mainly concerned with educating each of us to be a cog in the system rather than encouraging us to discover our own unique destiny. Whether the challenge of a growing awareness of lack of fulfilment is experienced as crisis or quest depends on our internal psychological and spiritual resources, and especially on our self-esteem.

When we do not feel confident, we retreat into a shell, not daring to risk rejection. We do not have the confidence to risk exposure, so we may keep many aspects of ourselves hidden. This reinforces an unbalanced concern with ourselves. Being crippled by awareness of our inadequacies and flaws makes us feel separate from others.

Many people try to deal with feelings of worthlessness by working in 'caring' professions, such as social work or teaching, but doing this does not necessarily heal an inadequate sense of self. A fundamental self-esteem is needed as a basis for being fully available to help others in the community.

Remedies for people stuck in this energy pattern help them to let go of a negative self-image by gaining a greater awareness of their value to the wider community.

Nina consulted me for arthritis and psoriasis, a skin condition that caused intense itching and burning in her pubic and anal area as well as inside her ear and on her elbows and knees. Whenever she brooded on her lot, the psoriasis became more inflamed and itchy. It had developed on her knee after an accident when she had split the skin there, but now patches had spread over most of her body. Her joints stiffened up overnight and in damp weather, and the inflammatory pains wandered from place to place. She was uncomfortable walking far, and anyway she had no energy. She appeared depressed, although she did not complain about this.

The joint troubles had started when she was ostracized by her fellow union members for working through a strike to keep a drop-in service open. 'I felt more commitment to the service users than to my colleagues.' She had paid a high price for sticking to her principles: she was ostracized by the workers she managed. They refused to speak to her except for practical purposes. 'I was extremely embarrassed by having more authority than them and it tapped into feelings I'd had for a long time about not deserving anything. I felt as if my skin was announcing, "I don't really deserve to be in this position – so don't take me too seriously!" Whether it's to do with my working-class background I don't know. I have always felt the need to prove myself, and I often feel worthless. I get depressed and I'm sure I drag my husband down.'

Nina was dogged by a lack of self-esteem, and the psoriasis embarrassed her by drawing attention in a negative way. She felt like a burden to her husband and children. She was aware that her lack of self-esteem created an unhealthy need for attention, yet she was still compelled to use it as a means of getting reassurance and affirmation.

I prescribed the remedy Baryta carbonica because of the underlying sense of inadequacy that motivated her community service. Baryta carbonica is a remedy for people who feel that their mental faculties are slow and that they are inferior, which makes them emotionally insecure and dependent.

Nina's joint pains were much better within a few weeks, and she became more mobile. The psoriasis took many months to clear up. Her skin condition did not improve until she was able to heal some of her old feelings of being unworthy, and to stop apologizing for her very existence. She needed to allow the nascent aware-ness that she was a valuable person to penetrate her consciousness.

OTHER REMEDIES

Ambra grisea	used when the person is extremely shy and comes out with foolish comments when embarrassed
Calcarea carbonica	healing for people who are slow at grasping things. People in this remedy pattern worry about their mental abilities and dread being exposed as 'frauds'.
Lac caninum	indicated for people who feel despised and internalize this as self-disgust. They may describe themselves as feel-ing unclean.

Silica   for people who feel shy and awkward in social situations, in spite of their keen observation of others and understanding of their motives. A lack of confidence about their work abilities makes them overly conscientious about details.

Soul Learning of Low Self-Esteem

Learn to accept and love yourself fully. Try extending to yourself the compassion you can feel for other people who are struggling.

Oppression

Oppression is a more severe situation than feeling trapped, when you actually are a victim rather than just feeling like a victim. When you feel trapped you are more likely to project your internal feelings of frustration and powerlessness outward, whereas when you feel oppressed you are more likely to be seriously restricted. Classic oppressive situations include where women are stuck in patriarchal relationships in which they are treated with disrespect, or worse, and where children are used, abused, beaten or bullied.

We know from the experiences of survivors that some people find unexpected resources inside themselves. A major preoccupation is how to deal with a crisis of faith in which the foundations of life have been pulled away. When I worked as a homeopath in the Palestine hospital in Cairo, I treated many people who had been displaced through political troubles and armed conflict in the region. Individuals dealt with very real issues around survival in a variety of ways. I was impressed at how much strength and integrity people displayed in the face of political oppression. The hospital where I worked was itself under threat from the Egyptian authorities, but, instead of assuming a victim stance, the management found creative solutions to the manifold problems confronting them on a daily basis, so that they could continue to go on providing first-class treatment for their patients.

Likewise, I have been awed by the fortitude of the orthodox Jews I have treated in Stamford Hill, London, some of whom are holocaust survivors. Some survivors talk about finding unexpected resources inside and, surprisingly, experience the grace of finding faith despite their awful circumstances.

Rachel was a Jewish woman who had developed post-partum psychosis, a syndrome where women become extremely agitated after childbirth. When I made a home visit to treat her, however, it emerged that her husband was even more destabilized. David was pacing up and down the hallway in a very agitated manner when I came to the house, talking volubly and exclaiming, 'I feel like a holocaust survivor.' From his monologue, he seemed to be taking the collective experience of his people on to his shoulders – which was clearly overwhelming him. He was physically restless, with trembling legs. His agitation had been triggered by his wife's post-partum illness and the responsibilities of his growing family. A self-employed businessman, he was anxious about his financial status and felt unable to carry on. David was not sleeping at all, and just wanted to walk and talk constantly about how terrible he was feeling. Even in the past he had never been able to keep his problems to himself, and he was unable to work on his own all day since a tremendous state of anxiety would build up if he tried. His long-term anxieties had erupted in an acute episode alongside his wife's illness. The way he resonated with the collective nature of suffering found expression when his wife was ill.

The similarity of Rachel's and David's states was quite striking. However, they each needed different remedies. I prescribed David the remedy Tarentula hispanica, which relieved him greatly. For Rachel, in an agitated state because she had not slept for the three months since the baby had been born, I prescribed Calcarea carbonica. Up to that point she had not been producing enough milk, and she had worked herself up into a state of acute anxiety. She was weepy and agitated and also needed to talk constantly. She hated to be alone and was not happy being stuck in the house with the baby. She felt exhausted, sick, dizzy and irritated. She knew she needed to get outside in the fresh air but felt too weak to go more than a few steps.

Rachel responded brilliantly to the homeopathic remedy, which calmed her down within a few days. Because she was then less panicked, she became able to breathe more easily, and she stopped having palpitations at night. Rachel still felt too hot in warm rooms, but the remedy went on to improve her temperature mechanism and also to regulate her bowels, which had become constipated since the birth.

Christine, a 16-year-old girl, came to see me because of her extremely painful periods and acne condition that flared up badly before each period. Unusually, for someone so young she had come to see me without her parents' knowledge. During our discussion it emerged that her father was very controlling and behaved in a tyrannical manner towards her. Christine had become depressed since her father was always shouting at her and attempting to control her, for instance by forbidding her to go out of the house except to school or to her job. She worked evenings and weekends in poorly paid jobs just to get out of the house, and as a result she was too tired to study.

A very bright girl, Christine was desperate to go into further education as a way of getting out of the oppressive home atmosphere. Her father seemed to be paranoid about her emerging sexuality and potential attractiveness. He was convinced that letting her off his firm leash would mean she would start seeing boys. This restrictive control meant that she was not able to develop any friendships at all. She felt isolated and depressed, crying all the time, and she was unable to share her feelings about her predicament with anyone else. She was trapped because she was still at school and unable to move out of the house.

In spite of her problems, Christine was charming and helpful to others, never appearing a burden but, in fact, almost too eager to please. She worked hard to improve her lot, but she seemed driven and desperately unhappy. I gave her the remedy Arsenicum album, in part because she was fastidiously tidy, in what seemed to be an attempt to gain some sense of control over her life by controlling the only thing she was able to – her immediate environment.

Christine's way out was through hard study. She had to give up any attempts at a social life with her fellow students. Her irrepressible, bubbly character had no outlet, but by suppressing her need for sociability she managed to win the trust of her father, so that her living situation became more tolerable. She struggled with the sheer amount of work she had to do and the lack of support to achieve its completion. But she did quite well in her exams and was offered a place at the university of her choice, an 'acceptable' reason to move out of the family home.

Christine's painful periods and acne improved as she managed to pursue the path she had hacked out in the face of so much opposition. She had never been able to explore her feelings about her emerging sexuality or even allow herself to think about boys, and I felt that this was part of the reason why her periods had been such a problem. Developing an awareness of herself as a woman was central to her path of healing, but she was not able to do that until she was finally able to move away from her father's watchful gaze. Her admirable persistence and fundamental resistance to the oppressive circumstances of her life meant that she was eventually able to find a way out of her situation through further education.

OTHER REMEDIES

Carbo vegetabilis	for people who feel negative and depressed. When they are sick, their energy levels become very low, and feelings of apathy and indifference take over. They may lash out at others with cutting remarks.
Causticum	for people who develop an intense sense of injustice due to their emotional sensitivity, and for those who have the ability to empathize with the sufferings of others
Lycopodium	a good remedy for people who feel fearful and cowardly; they get bullied because they feel unable to stand up to an oppressor.
Medorrhinum	indicated where the person cannot tolerate restraint and becomes wild and rebellious
Moschus	helpful for people who feel anxious and angry, with fits of rage erupting when they are under pressure. They may suffer from asthma and feel as if they will suffocate with the intensity of their feelings.
Pulsatilla	used where the person has collapsed into being a victim
Staphysagria	helpful where the person is frustrated and tries to create an escape through romantic fantasies

| Thuja | used for people who feel that their legs have been meta-phorically cut away from under them |

Soul Lesson of Oppression

Try to be open to the experience of grace in the face of a situation that appears intransigent or hopeless.

Panic Attacks

Panic attacks can occur when you feel overwhelmed and fearful of the challenges in your life. They are usually connected to a feeling of having no control over events, and this proves very scary. The emotion of fear engenders yet more fear, and you get locked into a fight, flight or play-dead response (where you freeze in an effort not to attract danger).

The constricted breathing typical of a panic attack is a symbol of resistance to the subconscious psychological material threatening to erupt into consciousness. The word 'anguish' derives from the Latin for narrowing or choking, and feelings of anguish explain the sensation of constriction in the throat. Of course, feeling that you cannot breathe properly is also guaranteed to bring on panic.

Manuella had treated her immigrant parents with something approaching disdain when she was growing up, an attitude born of her embarrassment at being a foreigner in England. Manuella had felt stupid and unpopular at school, and as she approached adolescence she had begun to drink alcohol because it helped her to feel funnier and more confident socially.

When she was 12, she had had a precocious sexual relationship. Her father found out and was furious, and he moved the family away to a new area. Manuella blamed herself for this and internalized her feelings of shame. This was when the panic attacks started. Later, when things started going badly for her in her job and her relationship, she became more and more phobic.

By the time she came to see me (when she was in her twenties) she could barely walk down a street without worrying about what she might do if she suddenly collapsed. She was convinced her heart would give out if she exerted herself in any sort of exercise, and she felt too anxious to try changing her job by going for interviews, because she felt she would not be able to control her nervousness. All her attention had been focused on how others saw her, and she was always worrying about what would happen if she was overcome with panic. She could not trust herself to let go and would hyperventilate.

Coming to see a homeopath was Manuella's first step in the process of paying more attention to her inner voice rather than what others might think. This is the first step to living more in the present, rather than responding in old habitual ways. I prescribed the remedy Kali arsenicum, which improved her symptoms and allowed her to stop focusing exclusively on her physical state and explore how to manage her strong emotions.

Kali arsenicum is a remedy homeopaths give for panic states where people are anxious about their hearts. Manuella had been so sure that her heart would give out that she had had numerous investigations carried out. Even when the consultant reassured her that there was no physical basis for the tachychardia (rapid heart rate), she was reassured for only a few days.

As she improved, Manuella discovered that underneath the panic lay a lot of rage: whenever she felt less panicky, a lot of anger would well up. The palpitations were actually the result of her attempt to control her anger. She was afraid of the intensity of her emotions, so she directed them against herself and they came out in the form of panic attacks. She realized that she needed to acknowledge her anger and rage in order to free up the energy that was locked in the frozen posture demanded by her fears. Underneath the anger were her old feelings of powerlessness and shame. She had felt deeply ashamed from an early age and had projected this shame onto her parents.

Gradually, over a period of months, Manuella was able to tolerate feeling angry without having to blame anyone else. She became less panicky and started examining unsatisfactory aspects of her life. Although on one level she felt she deserved things to be better, on another she had accepted her dissatisfaction because she felt unworthy and full of shame. Both feelings were to do with what she interpreted as her own self-centredness. 'I always take things personally rather than accept them as they are. I don't enjoy my life because I can't relax and let go.'

On her path to healing, Manuella had to regain a sense of worth and power, which meant altering all the situations she had created in her life that kept her in a position of powerlessness. She was in an unhappy relationship with someone who did not appreciate her or treat her with respect. The relationship did not nourish her, and she and her partner had not made love for over a year. Although he was living in her flat, she did not feel able to ask him to leave. She was also afraid of being on her own in London.

In spite of her fear of making changes, Manuella felt much better once she gathered up her courage and got another job. Instead of reverting to feeling out of control and panicky, she now felt even better. Her boss and workmates were much more pleasant than those in her old job, and she felt validated as a useful human being. She needed to have a positive sense of herself reinforced by those around her while she built up her fragile self-esteem. The process of building up a damaged self-esteem often takes years, and Manuella was still in treatment three years later.

OTHER REMEDIES

Aconite	used for panic attacks that have started after a shock, such as being in or witnessing a nasty accident. The shock results in panic attacks at night, often when going to sleep. People in this remedy pattern may have a fear of the dark and experience great anxiety about being left alone. During the panic attacks, they are convinced that death is imminent. They are often claustrophobic and may no longer be able to drive.
Argentum nitricum	helpful for panic attacks with agitation. People in this remedy pattern feel very hurried and anxious, with fears manifesting themselves almost as impulses. For instance, on a rooftop or cliff they may have a feeling of being drawn to the edge. They suffer from compulsive thoughts that something terrible will happen. The panic attacks

	become much worse when they are anticipating a meeting or social situation.
Arsenicum album	indicated for panic attacks with hypochondria. For these people, every little twinge is assumed to be a symptom of disease, regardless of how many times doctors reassure them that nothing is wrong. They may feel neurotic anxiety that loved ones have been involved in an accident when they are only late home. They hate to be alone.
Stramonium	for panic attacks that have started after some violent confrontation, such as a mugging or physical attack. The feeling during the panic attack is one of pure terror. People in this remedy pattern hate to be alone, especially at night. They are usually too afraid to sleep without the light on, and they may have terrifying nightmares.

Soul Lesson of Panic Attacks

You need to relax into the flow that is life. Everything changes constantly. By letting go of your attachment to the security you find in trying to control things, you can learn to go with the current of life rather than trying to obstruct it.

Pride

Pride can emerge from an affirmative sense of self-worth that is based on self-knowledge and self-acceptance. It comes from working on oneself and knowing the value of yourself and others. This can actually be a form of humility, in which you accept your role and place in the world. You know the meaning of your life, and value what you personally have to contribute to others.

Pride can become negative when you over-identify with your positive attributes and attempt to deny your imperfections. For instance, you can be too proud to apologize to others because you don't want to admit your faults.

Pride is a strategy that your ego uses to defend your self-image when you are feeling insecure. It is a means of compensating for a lack of self-worth, and can be very effective because most people are taken in by this kind of haughty bluff. In this case, pride is associated with arrogance, where you over-value your personal achievements in comparison to those of others. Scratch the surface and there's a sense of inadequacy or failure underneath.

Judith, a woman of 47, came to see me because of the discomfort of her uterine fibroids, which she wanted help in managing while she waited for them to shrink during her menopause. She was definitely pre-menopausal, with lengthening menstrual cycles and vaginal dryness. She had not made love with her husband for two years, although she said that companionship had always been more important in their relationship than sex.

Judith was looking for a change of direction in her life. Although very able and competent in a wide range of areas, she could not find the kind of work that would really inspire her. She had worked as a photographer in her early twenties, but had sacrificed her career for marriage, even though she had been concerned that her husband was not as well educated as she was. She became very involved with the Transcendental Meditation (TM) movement, organizing activities and teaching. But she had gradually become disillusioned with TM, and it was around this time that the symptoms associated with her fibroids had started. She felt frustrated, knowing that she was a good organizer but aware that she was not sufficiently diplomatic to handle organizational conflict. She started training as a teacher but felt that teaching did not really have enough professional status to satisfy her.

Judith was ambitious, but also had a soft nature. She described herself as 'yielding', especially in her relationship. She tended to go along with whatever her husband and daughter wanted. She was concerned about the impression she made on others and hated to attract any kind of criticism.

I gave her the remedy Palladium, made from the metal of the same name. People needing this remedy tend to be very sensitive to what other people think of them and very concerned about maintaining others' good opinion. Much of Judith's dissatisfaction in life seemed to stem from a feeling that she was not being properly valued. She always felt that her positive qualities were not properly recognized by others or weren't being properly channelled into fulfilling work. She felt as if the things she was doing were somehow 'beneath her', which is a feature of the remedy pattern requiring a remedy made from precious metals such as Palladium.

It was Judith's frustration that made her lash out, causing her to make 'undiplomatic' statements at times. Her disagreement with the Transcendental Meditation organization had its roots in this sense of being undervalued, and the ensuing frustration was implicated in her developing fibroids.

Remedies such as Palladium and Platinum help people deal with an inflated sense of pride which gets in the way of their ability to evaluate a situation accurately. In Judith's case, her overdeveloped sense of pride had prevented her not only from finding out what made her truly happy, but also from feeling that any occupation could truly be a source of happiness.

Erica, a woman needing Platina, had also been involved in meditation practice for many years. She said she had been fortunate enough to marry a wealthy barrister, and they lived with their grown-up children in the most expensive part of London. She had been able to devote herself to spiritual matters and meditation for many years.

However, she complained of disconcerting out-of-body experiences, which her teachers described as being due to an imbalance of kundalini energy (the energy believed by yoga practitioners to reside at the base of the spine) released through her meditation practice. She had never managed to find a teacher who could give her other practices to use that would control the unpleasant and disorienting kundalini sensations. Disillusioned, she began to search for the best holistic health care practitioners. She originally sought the help of a colleague of mine, who she had heard was an extremely good homeopath. In spite of the fact that many of her symptoms improved under his care, she explained that she had changed homeopaths because she resented paying him for her follow-up visits, which she felt were not necessary. Surprised that she did not seem to value the good care she had received, particularly in view of her apparent wealth, I explained that she could come in for follow-ups whenever she felt it would be appropriate, and we discussed her problems at length.

The threads of pride and dissatisfaction together ran through Erica's story in a similar way to those in the Palladium case. But in Platina situations, the concern to obtain the very best in every area is indicative of an over-developed ego. Given that the spiritual practices of every path are aimed at developing consciousness at the *expense* of ego, I reasoned that the energetic disturbances Erica described might be the result of a conflict between the mundane concerns of the ego and the more refined energies she was trying to develop.

OTHER REMEDIES

Dulcamara	recommended for the head of the family when they become insufferably controlling or domineering, thinking they know better what's best for everyone else in the family
Lycopodium	helps bombastic people who like to dominate in the domestic arena
Sulphur	used for people who are full of intellectual arrogance
Veratrum album	indicated for people who need to make up stories about their background or their social connections in order to make themselves appear to have a higher social status

Soul Lesson of Pride

Practise humility, even as you refine positive personal attributes as you journey through life.

Relationship Problems

Many of us have problems creating and sustaining intimate sexual relationships. We agonize over issues such as what men and women want and how we can find ways to relate well with each other. We have a much more demanding notion of partnership than our parents had, yet we are equipped with few tools to enable us to realize our ideal of romantic love. There is little support in our society for helping us resolve relationship problems in such a way that our soul grows.

Our notion of love has also been influenced by a psychological model of human beings as made up of a bundle of needs. What we call love is more often an expression of need. When your partner experiences your neediness, it awakens his or her fear of being trapped in a position of responsibility for meeting all your requirements. Another problem with this model is that you assume you should move on and try your luck with someone else, if a current partner is not fulfilling your desires, rather than re-examining the way you are relating.

Loving means opening your heart to love rather than trying to make the other person responsible for your ability to access loving feelings in yourself. In order to open your heart, you have to let go of your own needs and fears. Intimacy means being emotionally connected with your partner. When you feel more connected, there is, paradoxically, a greater sense of spaciousness in the relationship. The art of intimacy is to remain in the present moment as much as possible, rather than being distracted by fantasies, power struggles or problems that are ancient history. You may need to lighten up, and to learn not to take things too seriously.

We have relationships for a variety of reasons: in some cases to create a family and bring up children, in other cases to heal deep emotional wounding, in yet others to learn something specific. If your relationship is about a deep healing on the soul level, you will find yourself in one that functions as a crucible for transformation – which may not be easy or relaxing. It can be helpful to ask yourself what the soul lesson might be of the relationship you find yourself in. Understanding its deeper meaning can help you make appropriate choices about how to manage problem areas.

Homeopathic remedies can heal the wounds made by past or present relationships which may have resulted in feelings of loss, abandonment, grief, bitterness, defensiveness or guilt. Such feelings block your ability to be fully present in the current relationship. Old wounds in a relationship can destroy the heart of a loving connection, leaving couples barely functioning in a reduced shell of a relationship, polarized into victim and persecutory positions in the way they relate to each other.

Julie had been living in a difficult marriage for several years but did not know how to get out of it. She and her husband were attracted to each other when they met on a retreat at a spiritual centre in France, but she felt disappointed to discover that her husband was a money-making workaholic, with traditional expectations of a wife. He was well off, and she was full of fears about how she would manage financially if she left the marriage. The distance between them was exacerbated when Julie fell in love with someone else while on another retreat, but she did not know how much those feelings were reciprocated.

She had had a long history of oscillating moods, so now she plunged into a state of breakdown where she wept constantly and was almost too afraid to leave the house. As evening would approach, Julie would become intensely fearful, her body literally trembling with fear. She was unable to concentrate on anything requiring logical thinking: she could no longer read the lessons from her spiritual teacher or even keep up with paying household bills. 'I could just about cope with preparing a meal, for while I'm sitting at the table with my family things feel normal.' She hated to be on her own and needed company. She was full of self-criticism and hatred, and suicidal thoughts plagued her.

Julie was hospitalized for a time and then put on medication to allow her to return home. During her breakdown, Julie was tormented by the thought that she had to make a final decision about her marriage, but this was not the time to put herself under further stress. She told me that she always became dependent, childlike and yielding in a relationship. 'I feel like a little girl, and I'm afraid to ask questions because I'm easily hurt.'

Before even contemplating looking after herself alone, Julie needed treatment for her psychiatric crisis. She could only reach a decision when she was stable, and no longer assailed by fears, depression and terrible feelings of inadequacy.

She took the homeopathic remedy Calcarea carbonica during the period of breakdown, because of her intense fearfulness and inability to be around others. This sensitivity to exposure verged on a feeling of paranoia and is mirrored in the deep feeling of vulnerability common to those who need this remedy. Taking it diminished her intense insecurity and lack of self-esteem. Her heavy mood lifted and the suicidal thoughts eased off as her state of fear dissipated under the healing action of the remedy.

Julie was still fearful about the future, though, and sat wringing her hands as she talked about her fear of being left, of poverty and destitution. These fears seemed to stem from her experience as a teenager when her mother had lost everything and the family was very poor. I gave her the remedy Kali bromatum, which homeopaths prescribe when a person is intensely agitated and feels both fearful and isolated. Julie's state of anxiety was so intense that she literally shook with terror. She had not been able to sleep for months.

Wringing and picking at the hands while talking is a clear indication for this remedy, which is used to help people in states of deep psychological distress. The remedy dealt with Julie's psychotic state of agitation, and as she calmed down she started to work out strategies to deal with her fraught situation. She stopped worrying so much about the future and tried to concentrate on what was in front of her. When her husband saw how much better she was, he became more supportive and offered to find a place for her to live for a year while they negotiated a divorce settlement. Taking the remedy helped her accept she could no longer rely on the security provided by the relationship, and she decided to use the time to live independently, going abroad to stay with friends. She spent some time living apart from her husband but without breaking up the marriage, while she worked on her deep issue of dependency. She felt that she had a stronger sense of self after going through the breakdown and coming out the other side. It was as if her soul was more evolved as a result of facing her fears: the whole painful process had actually served to facilitate her spiritual growth.

OTHER REMEDIES

Ignatia	may be indicated where unrequited love has left the person with an emotional coldness
Medorrhinum	helpful where the failure to achieve and sustain intimacy has created a retreat from intimacy into sexual promiscuity. People in this remedy pattern prefer the excitement of sex to the possible demands of emotional connection and commitment.
Natrum muriaticum	for people who have been left depressed and brooding after the hurt and disappointment sustained in the breakdown of an intense emotional connection. They vow that they will not let the same thing happen again, and other

people have to work hard to get close to them. They can be prickly and oversensitive to the way others treat them, sometimes taking innocent comments the wrong way.

Sepia

indicated where an increasing sense of separation and emotional detachment has built up in a relationship, even though the person does not have the energy to pull away and finish the relationship. People in this remedy pattern are completely disinterested in sex and may feel emotionally dead.

Staphysagria

used where the frustration of trying and failing to connect in a relationship leads to a retreat into a fantasy world. The fantasies are about finding romantic love, but people in this state are too scared to risk relating to potential partners in the real world.

Soul Lesson of Relationship Problems

Creating intimacy means engaging fully with others in the here and now.

Sexual Problems

Many people need to heal their sexuality as a result of a history of difficult experiences, and for this reason sexual problems need to be handled with sensitivity and tenderness.

Sexual problems are rarely just about sex. Sexual boredom, low sexual desire and lack of intimacy are commonplace complaints among couples. Most of these problems are to do with the fears that closeness paradoxically causes. Sharing our lives with another makes us all too aware of the inevitability of loss. Many couples try to alleviate such feelings by forging a strong alliance that provides emotional security for each partner. This apparent closeness can cause its own problems because of the way emotional differences have to be suppressed. Not being honest in our communicating is the surest way to prevent intimacy developing, and therapists all agree that real intimacy is what we need in order to explore our full sexual potential.

The longing for love and tenderness is a casualty of today's 'performance' culture, which limits our erotic potential to genital pleasure. Sex therapy, the medical answer to sexual dissatisfaction, avoids this tricky problem, opting instead for the easier job of promoting more effective sexual techniques or 'wonder drugs' such as Viagra. Yet suggestions about new techniques and asking for what you want in bed do not work if underlying emotional issues are not addressed. As I discussed in my book on Tantric sex, sexual exploration can evolve into an awareness of the sacredness of love-making, in which sex becomes a conscious means to worship your beloved and gives you both an experience of merging into unity.

Mark, a middle-aged man, came to see me because he could not get an erection with his new, much younger partner. She was a dynamic, go-getting professional who had won a prestigious award in her field. Mark was past his prime, balding and with a spreading waistline. He confessed that, although his partner was eagerly discussing plans to set up house together, he was plagued with anxiety about whether she might go off with someone younger and more attractive. In truth, he did not feel man enough to be her lover. I gave him the remedy Lycopodium for the lack of confidence underlying his anxiety. In spite of the fact that he was a successful businessman in his own right and generally seen as a powerful person, Mark's relationship exposed his Achilles' heel – his underlying fear that he was actually inadequate.

The remedy dealt with these intimations of inadequacy and, unsurprisingly, getting and maintaining an erection were no longer problems. When he came for a follow-up appointment, Mark informed me that he and his partner had toasted me in bed after successfully making love. I do not know how long term their relationship went on to be, but I do know that fear was no longer inhibiting Mark's sexual expression.

Deborah developed lichen sclerosis, a condition in which the skin of the vulva thickens as a result of hormonal changes, making the vagina dry and sex painful. In her case the symptom was clearly connected to blocked sexual expression, an area she had neglected in spite of being in a committed relationship with someone she loved deeply.

During our discussion, Deborah recalled a lengthy period of sexual harassment at work, which still angered her greatly. She had found it difficult to trust men and had been involved with women for many years. Finally she had met and fallen in love with a man, much to her own surprise, but the sex was not working in their relationship.

On her path to healing, Deborah's first step was to heal the anger she still felt about past events. I gave her the remedy Nux vomica, because she had reacted to this infringement of her personal boundaries with rage. She had had to bury her rage at work, and had been so successful that she had virtually forgotten what had happened. Yet she recognized now how her deep anger had been, directed at all men. In spite of loving her partner, she still had not forgiven men, as a general category, for the specific harassment that had happened to her.

Catherine came to see me because she was worried about succumbing to bulimia, an obsessional cycle of comfort eating and self-induced vomiting which she felt she had successfully overcome during her twenties, but which kept re-emerging at times of major stress. After seeing a psychotherapist for some time, Catherine had realized that her condition was connected with being forced to perform oral sex on her father as a child. She described how her father had been tremendously demand- ing emotionally, and created a 'special' relationship with her as he had not been getting his needs met by her mother. Now Catherine feels a great deal of panic as she begins to get close in a relationship and experiences the urge to stuff herself with food, then feels so disgusted with herself that she has to make herself vomit. She can handle sex only if it is about lust rather than intimacy.

Abuse sexualizes the person at an early age, so that young people end up in situations they cannot handle emotionally and get abused further. Not having any experience of being able to maintain personal safety, their sense of boundaries later tend to be very weak. Because an abuser behaves inappropriately, the abused person often ends up trying to take on responsibility for the whole situation; this is particularly unfair and difficult because they feel so weak and vulnerable as a result of the abuse.

It is a long journey back to feeling safe enough to explore your own sexuality without fear. In sex, it is important to be able to say no to anything you don't want to do, so that eventually you feel secure enough to say yes to the experiences that you do want.

With the help of the homeopathic remedy Natrum muriaticum, Catherine went through the long, painful process of recovering her early memories and allowing herself to feel all the terror of what had happened to her. When her distressing memories returned, she was plunged into tremendous anger and depression. Because of her vulnerability, she had tried to keep those memories firmly unconscious. As a result, that energy was not available for her life. The path of healing involved accepting the memories, and then letting go of her past wounds sufficiently to enable her to relate to men according to the present situation rather than the past.

Her psychotherapy gave her a place to explore these difficult feelings, while the remedy lifted her out of a deep depression and also improved her attitudes towards food. Remedies like Natrum muriaticum are deep acting and work slowly, healing psychological and physical wounds over a matter of months or years, depending on how long you have been stuck in your particular energy pattern.

OTHER REMEDIES

Bufo	used for people who are obsessed by masturbating.
Caladium	helps men who are impotent in spite of a strong sexual interest
Conium	for people whose sexual drive is suppressed when they are forced into celibacy and have not chosen that path, for instance, when their partner dies. They may close down emotionally and feel flat and depressed or hard and uncaring.
Fluoric acid	helps people who lustfully eye up members of the opposite sex all the time. They have 'only one thing on their mind'.

Hyoscyamus	used where the sexual drive feels intensely overwhelming but impossible to satisfy. They may behave in exhibition-ist ways.
Kali bromatum	useful where a history of childhood abuse leaves the person in a state of isolation, terror or even paranoia. They become physically agitated when distressed.
Lycopodium	for people who suffer from commitment phobia, in which the fear of commitment creates a search for physical rela-tionships rather than emotional and soul connections. Many men in this remedy pattern develop problems with sexual performance because of their fear of intimacy.
Medorrhinum	helpful where the desire for sex replaces the drive for intimacy
Onosmodium	indicated where people are so preoccupied with sex that they feel they can't focus on the rest of their life. They feel apathetic and directionless.
Origanon	used for women whose clitoris is so sensitively irritated that it can't be touched during love-making
Staphysagria	indicated for people who find it difficult to satisfy their desire for romance in the mundane world

Soul Lesson of Sexual Problems

In order to unite sex, heart and soul, try to consciously nurture your soul through your sexual relationship.

Shock

A near escape from death or serious injury can leave you in the traumatic after-math of shock. A specific trauma can produce shock, as can a long period of 'life' stress, whether domestic, financial or illness-related. Other common trig-gers include car accidents, falls, surgery and emotional crises. Any situation in which you are helpless to affect the outcome of events is one that is likely to cause symptoms.

What these circumstances have in common is the way they shatter your sense of safety, making you aware of how precarious life really is. The mere thought that you could die at any moment is especially likely to instil panic and fear, unless you have come to terms with your mortality. A common reaction is 'dissociation', where you try to cut off from an unpleasant experience by blocking it out. The problem with this solution is that part of you remains frozen in the process.

Many traumatized people experience a slow decline in their ability to deal with both old and new stresses until they find a way of mastering troublesome past experiences. Small upsets in everyday life can restimulate shock or panic, causing reactions ranging from mild jitteriness to extreme fear. Because the endocrine (hormonal) and sympathetic nervous systems remain overstimulated, a variety of symptoms can develop, often starting some months after the trigger. Typical of delayed shock are panic attacks, depression and other emotional reactions that feel beyond your control, such as numbness in parts of the body, amnesia, fainting, dizziness and poor concentration.

Agoraphobia or other phobias, obsessive behaviour, unexplained outbursts of anger, insomnia and stammering are also all key signs of buried shock. Other pointers include an oversensitive startle reflex or an inability to speak in groups without the help of a sedative or beta-blocker to calm a racing heart.

SIGNS OF SHOCK

- constantly reliving aspects of the trauma
- obsessively ruminating on what happened
- difficulty sleeping, often because thoughts or images keep intruding
- feelings of being 'wired up', tense and unusually irritable or angry
- avoidance of activities that remind you of the shock
- blanking out thoughts associated with the event

Ros, a 29-year-old woman, consulted me a few years ago for a panic disorder that had started five years previously after a car accident. She had been afraid of dying in the ambulance on the way to hospital, but, after a week of feeling bruised, stiff and heavy-headed, she went back to work. Several months later she developed a sensitivity to loud noises along with a generalized anxiety that something awful might happen at any moment. Often her heart raced, her body shook, a sensation of butterflies disturbed her abdomen and she couldn't eat. The panic these feelings induced was so acute that she could not go out alone.

After a range of medical tests failed to produce an explanation, Ros saw a psychiatrist for two years. She did not respond to either counselling or relaxation techniques, nor to the medication her doctor prescribed for the abdominal symptoms he had diagnosed as irritable bowel syndrome. Whereas she had once been very positive, sociable and independent, Ros had become depressed and weepy, and unable to leave the house without a close member of her family. 'I can't make any decisions – even about what to cook. Everything feels like a monumental dilemma. I feel aimless, I don't have any motivation to do things any more. I used to enjoy going out and seeing friends. Now I can't go anywhere on my own because I'm frightened what might happen if the panic comes over me.'

I started her treatment with Pulsatilla, the remedy that seemed most indicated for her state of emotional dependency and fearfulness. After a very short intensification of the panic symptoms the first night after taking the remedy, Ros began to feel much happier and more relaxed. She found herself smiling and even laughing. However, the good effects of the remedy were short lived. They wore off after a week, and when a repeat dose only lasted the same length of time I prescribed Aconite, one of the main homeopathic remedies for the delayed effects of shock. Ros' panic disorder showed that her sympathetic nervous system was still over-stimulated as a result of the initial trauma. This time the effect of the remedy lasted and, after a few repetitions, she has had no further panic attacks. 'For the first time in a long time I noticed how beautiful the garden was. Until then all my attention was focused on how bad I was feeling – I couldn't respond to colours or beauty. Sometimes the fear comes into my mind for a few seconds, but it doesn't affect me any more. It's just the memory of how I used to feel coming back to me.' Her tearful moods and irritability have disappeared, and she is able to enjoy her relationship with her husband once again. The irritable bowel syndrome also cleared up.

OTHER REMEDIES

Aconite	recommended after fright, where people feel overwhelmed by waves of anxiety and panic with the awareness that they might have died. The shock results in panic attacks at night on going to sleep. They are afraid of the dark and when left alone. They may develop panic attacks, and become convinced that death is imminent.
Arnica	recommended after physical injuries. People needing this homeopathic remedy typically have a stoical response to injuries. These are the people who get up after being knocked off their bicycles, saying 'I'm all right. There's really nothing wrong,' and riding off home as if nothing has happened. Some hours later, the panic and shakiness start coming out. Arnica helps to heal bruising and soft-tissue damage as well as the psychic shock.
Staphysagria	indicated where the person feels violated rather than shocked, especially after surgery
Stramonium	helpful after a person has survived a situation of pure terror, such as a violent attack or rape. It is also used for people who are suffering from panic attacks following such an experience. These people hate to be alone at night, and become too afraid to sleep without a light on. They have terrifying nightmares.

Soul Learning of Shock

Heal your body memories of trauma. Come to terms with your own mortality and re-affirm your desire to live.

Stagnation in Work

Feelings of stagnation can arise as a result of having inappropriate expectations of work. Dissatisfaction and constant complaining can be strategies of disengaging with work and keeping it at a distance. Perhaps the fact that you are resorting to such strategies is a sign that you are distancing yourself from what is happening in your life. A challenging method of clarifying whether it is really your work that is the problem, or yourself, is to re-engage with work. Try getting more involved in your job, and see what it feels like to take more interest. Sometimes you unexpectedly find that you care more about what you're doing, and you get more out of it. By putting more energy in, you get more out; you find value and meaning in what you are doing.

On the other hand, it may be that you need to get out of work, rather than get more into it.

The problem may be that you find yourself doing a job that you have not consciously chosen to do. You may have just put one foot in front of the other without questioning whether this was the occupation you wanted to follow. Perhaps your parents had ambitions for you and you unquestioningly followed their wishes. Perhaps you were good at certain subjects at school and got herded into following a particular career on that basis.

Feelings of stagnation are likely to arise if you haven't yet found a niche in which to express your talents. Work is an arena in which to define ourselves as individuals, through our own efforts. It's up to us to meet this challenge in whatever ways we can. Many people are no longer spending their lives in stable, conventional jobs. The ways we make a living are less structured than the ways our parents did so. Since the advent of better communications through faxes, mobile phones and the internet, many of us can access work from wherever we are and it can access us at any time. This situation can be tyrannical, driving us into states of workaholism, or it can be liberating, allowing us to create flexible structures that better suit our needs.

Work often expresses what we are doing with our lives. We need to know that we have made a choice that is congruent with our skills, talents and desires.

preparing for soul work

Work is liberating if you are lucky enough to make a living through ways of occupying yourself that express your interests, passions and commitment.

John came to see me with a nervous cough, which could be set off by any sort of emotion, from laughter and excitement to anxiety and depression. His skin rashes and allergic symptoms were also tied in with changes in his psychological state.

In his early forties, John had seen his marriage break down, and problems at work had led to a change of jobs in the world of banking. The change had not proved satisfying.

John had always been goal-oriented and ambitious. His long-term goal was to retire as early as possible, having made enough money to do so comfortably. Since things had not been as easy as he had hoped, he was plagued by a lack of self-confidence. Every time he had to face a challenge he became anxious about whether he could handle it, and more and more situations challenged him. When something went wrong, he felt personally attacked. This tied in with his marital problems: he had felt devastated by his wife having an affair, which damaged his self-esteem considerably. The positive by-product of his grief was that he rediscovered his emotions, crying for the first time in his life over losing his wife. After a period of counselling, he had attempted a reconciliation, but he felt even more devastated when their attempt to get back together was unsuccessful.

When I treated him with Lycopodium, John's confidence improved, and a new set of life goals emerged. He realized that he needed to change his work altogether and find something that was more congruent with his changing values. In fact they were not really changing, but he was becoming more aware, for the first time, of his fundamental priorities.

John needed to move out of banking and find ways to align work values with personal values. He wanted to increase his mental capabilities as well as his capacity for pleasure and relaxation, a goal that had been absent in previous ambitions. He wanted to settle in a village, build a wide range of friends, and practise some kind of healing art. He wanted to be fit and healthy now that he had regained his health and vitality with homeopathy. His top priority was to have a good relationship, and he tried to make a success of his new relationship with a younger woman, but she could not commit herself to it. He sold his house anyway and moved out of

London on his own, determined to pursue his new goals regardless of whether he was in a relationship or not.

Baryta carbonica	needed for people who feel a lack of motivation, becoming disengaged and mentally dull. They feel inadequate.
Calcarea carbonica	for people who too willingly accept the limitations of their job. As they put less into the job, their energy decreases and they find they have less to give.

Soul Lesson of Work Stagnation

You may need to exercise willpower, or acknowledge your own choices. Experiment with immersing yourself more deeply in your occupation before considering a change.

Workaholism

Workaholism results from an over-identification with work. You may be working long hours as an excuse to avoid uncomfortable feelings in your life – such as depression, loneliness, emptiness or inadequacy – throwing yourself into a work role you can hide behind. Underneath there may be fears of being exposed or of not being recognized and validated. You may be afraid of being found out to be no good at what you are doing. You may not have the self-esteem to ask for what you want.

You may feel safer trying to get your emotional needs met at work than in the world of relationships. If this is the case, your craving to be seen and valued at work cannot be satisfied because you really need to look for satisfaction in your personal life. Likewise, if your experience of deprivation and lack of nurturing is projected onto objects – so that you have a need to amass material goods and wealth as a compensation – your search for emotional satisfaction is doomed to fail.

Part of the need to identify with your work role is the fact that, in contemporary society, social roles are ill-defined. Work may be one of the few areas where you feel sure of your identity, and an arena in which you can construct an uncomplicated persona.

Sporadic workaholism, where you throw yourself into projects with enthusiasm for a limited period of time, can be quite healthy. Your feel-good body chemicals, the endorphins, are stimulated through intense involvement in your work – but this approach needs to be balanced by periods of rest, where you focus on other aspects of your life.

In a chronic workaholic pattern you're more likely to be driven by insecurity, or guilt that you can't get through the ever-increasing mountain of work in front of you. One man told me, 'I feel like I'm still trying to impress my parents, even though they died years ago. In fact, maybe it's because they're dead I feel I want to prove myself even more.'

Ross, aged 43, had suffered from daily tension headaches for the last 20 years. Even laughing caused dizziness and aggravated his pain, and his legs felt weak when the headache was bad. His left shoulder was tense most of the time; the left was also the side where he got the headaches. He had tried the conventional medicines on offer, but the only time his headache seemed any better was while he meditated. He had been meditating for a year and a half, but as soon as he finished each session the headache came straight back.

A stressed-out businessman, Ross had been working hard for several years. He felt drained and tired a lot of the time and was very irritable with the constant demands of running his own business. He complained, 'I get angry at the smallest thing. I especially hate seeing a lack of discipline in others.' His wife described him as very critical and difficult to please.

His remedy, Nux vomica, was chosen because of his intolerance for what he perceived as others' shortcomings. He had an arrogant attitude and assumed that no one else could do things as well as he could. Yet he also felt resentful at the burdens he took on himself as a result of this attitude. While on the outside he behaved in a easy-going and courteous manner, on the inside he felt driven and harassed.

Straight after taking the first dose of Nux vomica, his headache 'miraculously disappeared that instant'. He told his wife that evening, 'It feels like the right solution. It just took all the pain and tension around my face and head away.'

I asked what difference he noticed when meditating from his normal state. He explained that he felt better because he was no longer feeling separate from others; however, when he stopped, he immediately slipped back into his normal mode of being critical and therefore separate. After taking the remedy, Ross was able to maintain this sense of connectedness even without meditating.

'My headache disappeared completely and has recurred only occasionally since then. My energy is a lot better, and I don't feel tired after eating as I used to. My nose used to be blocked all the time, and that has opened up since the treatment. I used to be more anxious and angry. It was as if there was a war going on inside me. Now I feel a lot calmer in spite of the fact there's a lot of turmoil at work. I've been handling my business problems much better.'

OTHER REMEDIES

Bryonia	for those who work hard because they worry a lot about their business affairs. Especially useful for people running their own company, who feel irritable and pre-occupied with problems at work.
Psorinum	for people who over-work as a result of deep fears about becoming destitute in later life
Tarentula hispanica	a remedy for people who feel driven. They work too much as a means of channelling their restless energy into something absorbing.

Soul Learning of Workaholism

You need to learn to see work as service. Think about how you can use work as a means of manifesting your soul, rather than as an arena in which your personal needs are met.

part 3

remedies for the soul

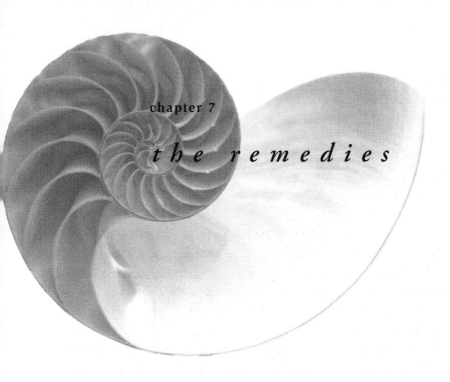

the remedies

In this section I shall give profiles of a small selection of the thousands of remedies that homeopaths use. I have chosen remedies that come up repeatedly in my practice to help people resolve the problematic issues in their lives.

For each remedy I first describe the energy pattern associated with that remedy. This is the pattern displayed by people who need this remedy in order to heal themselves. I then describe the cases of some of the people I have treated, in order to illustrate how someone with this energy pattern can be cured with the relevant homeopathic remedy.

Some of the improvements you can expect should you be prescribed this remedy will also be described, although you need to bear in mind that your response will be as unique as you are. Finally, I offer a soul lesson for each remedy, suggesting the possible learning that may be relevant to those who identify with this remedy pattern.

The remedy profiles are not intended as a resource for self-diagnosis. Finding the correct constitutional remedy for each person is a very complex task. It is something that needs to be done in conjunction with an experienced homeopath. A homeopath can also help you to discover what your own deepest issues are; this is something that is often difficult to do on your own. A homeopath will evaluate the sometimes turbulent changes that take place after taking a remedy, when the increased energy the remedy causes can bring repressed feelings to the surface. He or she can also decide when a further dose of your remedy needs to be given.

The remedy profiles are intended to help prepare readers for the soul work of homeopathic treatment by helping them to identify some of the principal places in which their energy may be blocked. We are affected by stuck energy patterns on many levels. The remedy profiles I present here are only small snapshots, which by no means cover all the possible ways these remedy patterns can manifest themselves in people's lives.

I have described the energy pattern of each remedy by describing the personality traits of people who are affected by that pattern. Your personality is a tool through which the work of the soul is done, just as your body is a tool for the soul. The personality is not the same thing as the soul. Because the soul is more fundamental, it is less tangible. Homeopaths look at your personality as a manifestation of your soul, and use this information about your character to find a remedy. What you are doing now in your life shapes your personality, together with the experiences that you have gone through in the past. Your character then shapes the way you respond to others, but you need to realize that the level of the personality is not the whole story. So as not to over-identify with our own particular problems, you need to go beyond the level of personality and connect with your soul. I will make some suggestions for ways to facilitate this deeper connection in my closing thoughts at the end of the section.

Homeopathic remedies do not change your personality traits: they just help you to loosen your attachment to habitual ways of responding. They enable you to respond to the situations you find yourself in more constructively. Remedies can help you to extract the positive lessons from challenging situations by helping you to view things from a different perspective. A more constructive way of looking at your difficulties is to see them as ways of helping you to become more conscious of the deeper truths in your life, and of the path that attracts you as a more soulful way of being in the world.

Your basic energy pattern is not unrecognizably altered by taking a remedy. What the remedy does is accentuate the positive rather than the negative aspects of your energy pattern. Taking a remedy does not fundamentally change you, it just allows you to be more yourself and let go of the obstacles hampering your full self-expression. It stimulates you to take wiser decisions, which helps you to evolve.

For example, if you have the easy facility with ideas of the Sulphur pattern, taking the remedy does not remove this, but will help you to be more discerning and focus on ideas that you can follow through. The remedy helps you to access your soul's desires so that you can pursue the projects that are really important to you.

Alternatively, if you resonate with the Natrum muriaticum pattern, intimate relationships are of primary importance to you, and taking the remedy can heal any resentful bitterness that you carry as a result of emotional wounding. The remedy will help you to forgive the person who hurt you, dissolve your armour, and allow you to open up to love again.

In describing the energy patterns of each individual remedy I have not concentrated on the physical symptoms associated with each pattern because they are not within the scope of this book. In rebalancing body, mind and soul, what needs treating is the energy body. Once energy is flowing freely again, everything else falls into place. Homeopathy can bring about the deep cure of an enormous range of physical illnesses. If the core energy disturbance is treated with the correct remedy, most symptoms will improve, unless the disease process is far advanced.

Aconitum Napellus

The energy pattern of Aconitum can be traced in the theme of shock. Extreme experiences such as those during war leave psychic scars and distort the energy body in the pattern of trauma, which often responds to shock remedies such as Aconitum or Stramonium.

The Aconitum energy pattern has frequently been grafted onto people through serious trauma, such as a near-death experience, or circumstances that jolt them into an awareness of mortality. For example, one person had a gun held to her head on a Paris metro during a mugging. Another had been making a routine parachute jump when his parachute failed to open; he survived only because a tree broke his fall. Another man had been working in London's Heathrow airport when a bomb exploded. These are the kinds of dramatic events that leave people in a state known as post-traumatic stress syndrome, a condition that often corresponds to the energy pattern of Aconitum and responds well to this remedy.

Serious car accidents are another typical instigator of this energy pattern: they leave the patient fearful of driving and nervous of being a passenger, and they tend to generate a host of other fears. The people affected become phobic, developing fears of death and darkness or claustrophobia on trains, in elevators and among crowds.

It is very important how people are cared for during a state of shock. They become hyper-sensitive, and in this state shock can be imprinted into the cellular memory of the body. When this occurs, the autonomic nervous system remains on red alert for years, and it kicks into fight or flight reactions whenever the person is under stress. Physiologically, the nervous and circulatory systems are on permanent overdrive, and people can have problems with palpitations or panic attacks.

For example, one woman went into a state of tremendous shock on leaving the police station where she had acted as a witness to her daughter reporting a rape. She cried nonstop for hours, feeling overwhelmed by rage and tormented with violent impulses towards the stranger who had committed this crime. When this subsided, she then slept heavily for nine hours, and the crisis seemed to be over. But when she had to sit tests as part of a Fine Arts course she was taking, a tremendous anxiety almost paralysed her. She needed Aconitum to release this.

For another person, old shock symptoms (after being attacked as a young man) were restimulated by the prospect of becoming a father. He found himself getting increasingly anxious during his wife's pregnancy, and he finally erupted into panic attacks for no apparent reason.

One adolescent suffered phobias about flying, travelling by train and even car journeys, all of which seemed to have started after he woke from sedation while still undergoing an operation to remove his tonsils. The operating theatre staff had panicked, and he clearly remembered someone saying he would die.

Sometimes the original trauma does not seem severe enough to imprint a shock state on our energy body, but the marker of residual shock is that we become more fearful and that panic is easily stimulated by the slightest stress. One man had to take beta-blockers every time he gave routine presentations at work. He traced his trauma to an early separation from his parents. He recalled screaming as the train pulled out of the station when he was sent away from home to boarding school.

All of these people were helped by the homeopathic remedy Aconitum. It treats people who are frozen in a posture of fear after some traumatic event. The common feature is that the person has had their life threatened, or the thought that they could die has entered their consciousness. At a conscious or subconscious level, they become tormented by the idea that they could die at any time. They feel better when they are in company, as they believe that others will protect them from harm.

Brian went into shock after a telephone call telling him that his father had collapsed with a stroke. His father had been over-stretched for some time in caring for Brian's sister, who suffered from cerebral palsy, and also his wife, who had become detached from the world because of the form of progressive dementia known as Alzheimer's Disease. Once his father collapsed, Brian was pulled back into the distressing family situation he had been avoiding because he found it so upsetting.

the remedies

After the phone call he had been unable to respond at all, and initially reacted with acute shock characterized by a denial of the severity of the situation. Over the next few months, he told me that he had plummeted into the deepest, most 'shadowed' part of himself. 'I lost the plot completely. It was like going into a dark cave which I couldn't get out of. I tried to face my demons connected with my difficult relationship with my father, my guilt about my sister and my sorrow at seeing my mother disintegrate.'

Old memories of abuse by a teacher at school during his early teens began to surface for the first time. Brian became aware that he had internalized a feeling of self-disgust. While he was going through this crisis, his chest felt tight and his breathing panicky. He felt depressed and guilt-ridden, and suffered a tremendous lack of confidence. Although Brian was a well-regarded musician and composer, it had always been difficult for him to feel he deserved his success, and he became tearful whenever anyone complimented him or was genuinely appreciative. His guilt over his disabled sister had prevented him from really being able to enjoy his life, and the experiences of abuse had imprinted a shock state on his body while he was still a youth.

In Brian's case, the remedy Aconitum released this imprinting through horrendous dreams in which he relived situations of sexual abuse and other scenarios over several weeks. After going through this period of processing painful memories, he emerged a lot stronger. He was no longer permanently frozen into a posture of fear, and his feelings of panic subsided. He felt able to allow the memories to resurface without feeling destabilized by them, and he started to accept his experiences as an unwelcome part of his history without being overwhelmed by them.

After taking the remedy, Brian regained a sense of pleasure in life. 'I'm ready for the real me to stand up. I've never had a chance before. I've always felt inadequate, and acted as if everything I did wasn't worth anything.'

Much personal art is concerned with working out inner psychological issues, and Brian was able to draw on his own experiences and use them as creative material. He was clear that he didn't want to create something that would reproduce the negativity in himself. Instead he reaffirmed his commitment to making music that would add positive meaning to people's lives. He wanted his compositions to add something of beauty to the world.

What to Expect as the Remedy Works

Taking this remedy heals memories of trauma which have been locked in the body at a cellular level, so that shock symptoms are no longer restimulated at the slightest stress. The remedy dissolves states of panic and fear. You no longer feel terrified at the thought of death, although the fact that the experience is by its very nature unknown, will still inspire awe in you.

When you are no longer in thrall to fear and panic, you can move on in your life. You achieve some peace with the events of the past, and you feel more in balance. Your open, sympathetic, caring nature becomes freed of the neurotic anxieties that have dogged you since your traumatic experience. You will become more self-sufficient, not needing someone to be around all the time in case they are required to save you. The remedy reinstates your normally resilient health. Because of your strong constitution, when well, you are a vigorous person who enjoys good health. By releasing your energy, the remedy will allow your natural optimism to re-establish itself.

Soul Learning for Aconite

Coming to terms with your mortality by accepting the transience of life, and learning to value living in the present.

Anacardium

The central theme of the Anarcardium remedy pattern is inadequacy. People who are in this energy pattern feel as if nothing they do ever turns out well. A taxi driver described it as 'being jinxed', with everything going wrong at the worst possible moment, from his cab breaking down to his marriage falling apart. This perception of powerlessness can be quite paralysing, preventing the person locked in this pattern from taking constructive steps to turn the situation around. Feeling like a victim creates a psychological passivity, which tends to lead to more situations where one is victimized.

If people are not able to create circumstances where things flow smoothly and creatively, a suspicion develops of things somehow always being out of place. It can be the conviction that they are never in the right place at the right time, or that they do not fit in with other people. People with this energy pattern feel dogged by a deep sense of alienation, of not knowing how to get close to others, and of not fitting into the wider social community. Not having the social skills necessary to form satisfying relationships with others, they can develop a deep sense of inadequacy, which is so painful to acknowledge that they try to cover it up.

This alienation results from a lack of emotional nurturing. Their emotional nature has withered away and is stunted. Children who have spent long years at boarding schools can get stuck in this pattern if they are not able to find loving resources in their environment to compensate for an early separation from their parents. Not having been loved enough as children, they may find it difficult to know what love is, and so it is very difficult for them to be loving. Instead, their relationships are based on the currency of power. Because their hearts are not open, they fall back on a sort of commodification of interaction: they are always asking themselves what they can get from other people, and how much others owe them. At an unconscious level, they feel that if they do express love to someone else, they will have less love left for themselves.

This self-centred survival strategy leaves little space for an awareness of the needs of others, and their natural generosity of spirit can become mean and punitive. Spiteful thoughts and desires predominate, sometimes coming to the fore when the person is feeling more powerful. One woman, who deeply resented having to care for her husband's ailing aged parent, had fantasies of putting marbles at the top of the stairs so that the unsteady old man would topple down them.

It is well known that those who humiliate or bully others have usually gone through these sorts of experiences themselves and are unconsciously perpetuating the same negative states. The pressure group for the victims of torture, Amnesty International, suggests that any of us can become brutal with others: all that is needed is that we go through brutalizing experiences ourselves. The pleasures of domination attract some of these people into sado-masochistic sexual practices. Through such games they re-enact the dynamics of power and powerlessness.

Anger often becomes internalized early on. Usually the anger is directed towards whatever circumstances have trapped a person into this situation, such as a distant father and inadequate mother unable to make up for the father's absence or harshness. This anger seeps out in a stream of negative thoughts, with frequent cursing, out loud or under the breath. This kind of pent-up anger can make Anacardium personalities quite vicious drivers who punctuate their driving with derogatory comments about other road users. This dog-eat-dog attitude means there is no space for compassion, one of the prime qualities of the soul. There is little compassion for their own struggling selves either, and they feel afraid to be stripped down and exposed. All this outer hardness hides a needy interior, where the person can feel desperate for contact.

Thomas, a teacher at a boys' preparatory school, had a strict disciplinary attitude. 'It amuses me that some boys are frightened of me. I glare at them. I'm certainly not going to go around smiling.' He even picked on a boy who found it difficult to concentrate because of his hyperactivity. 'I'm pretty unpleasant if someone crosses me. After I shouted when one boy talked in class, it was like a morgue for half an hour, which I rather liked.' He admitted to gaining pleasure from 'making an example of the boy', shouting at him and humiliating him wherever possible. The boy's mother had complained that Thomas was a bully, which just made him more vindictive.

Clearly there was a tremendous anger simmering under the surface; Thomas blamed others for his not getting the recognition he felt he deserved. When the headmaster expressed his dissatisfaction with Thomas' inflexible teaching style, he felt extremely angry in response and complained to his colleagues, criticizing the head for falling standards. Nonetheless, his being put on probation brought up old feelings of inadequacy, which manifested itself through frequent bouts of anxiety and irritability. Physically he suffered from a nervous cough and dryness, which made him clear his throat repeatedly. He was plagued by headaches. Perhaps predisposed due to his mother's history of diverticulitis, Thomas' digestion seemed over-sensitive and he complained of bouts of gastric discomfort. When he felt tense he suffered from indigestion and stomach pains.

I prescribed the remedy Anacardium because of the malicious streak in him. He was not good at relating to others: he lacked close friendships, and his isolation led to his making others' lives a misery. This is a deep problem, covering the core of the soul with misanthropic attitudes towards others. His path to cure involved healing this sense of isolation and defensiveness, allowing him to feel more compassionate towards himself, and therefore towards others.

Anacardium healed Thomas' inferiority complex so that he no longer felt so driven to prove himself. This need to prove himself was one of the things behind his need for strict discipline, which he felt was necessary to ensure that the boys paid him total attention.

Thomas was asked to leave the school, and he had to go through a period of reflecting on his attitudes and working at managing his anger better before being able to let go of his resentment and find another teaching post.

What to Expect as the Remedy Works

Anacardium helps to resolve a condition of inner conflict projected outwards in hostility. Taking the remedy allows you to reintegrate the harsh side that has become split off from your more vulnerable side. Once you no longer expend so much energy on this internal dialogue, you can focus on making constructive changes in your life. When you feel more compassionate towards yourself, you can be more tolerant of others.

Anacardium heals your deep inferiority complex, meaning that you are no longer driven to prove yourself. It stimulates your self-confidence. As you feel better about yourself you feel less aggressive towards others. If you no longer feel marginalized yourself, you do not want to persecute others. In dealing with other people, the remedy strengthens your internal sense of conscience so that your awareness of what is right and what is wrong provides another buffer against 'acting out' your own negative feelings in situations with others. You behave in ways that are congruent with your conscience. Most importantly, the remedy helps you to integrate the different parts of yourself through accepting and allowing the aspects you'd like to disown, as well as those you like.

Soul Learning for Anacardium

To deal with your lack of confidence, you need to learn to love yourself and others. Try to allow compassion to sweeten your soul.

Arsenicum Album

The energy pattern of Arsenicum album manifests itself in the central theme of anxiety. This is a neurotic anxiety that is free-floating, attaching itself to whatever happens to be relevant at that moment. There is a deep sense of insecurity, and the person is always worried that their circumstances will change for the worse. They are troubled by thoughts of some kind of disaster striking them: that they might lose their nearest and dearest, for example. It is very common for people in this remedy pattern to be panicked whenever their partner or children are late, immediately assuming the worst. Their mind goes into fast-forward, imagining the worst-case scenarios and wondering whether they should call the police or the hospital straightaway. Even when their partner is habitually late, the Arsenicum pattern encourages the mind to dwell on potential catastrophes.

One of the most crippling forms this anxiety takes is a hypochondriacal anxiety about health, which drives those affected to consult doctor after doctor and specialist after specialist, and to keep having investigative tests, some of which can be quite invasive. Routinely these tests reveal nothing pathological, and the person feels temporarily reassured. But within a short period of time the anxiety builds up again and becomes uncontrollable.

Anna was overly anxious about a pain in her chest, a symptom which is extremely common in people who are physically tense, although many people worry about it as a possible indicator of heart trouble. In spite of repeated electrocardiograms to check her heart, the results of which were negative, she continued to worry about the pain. It emerged that years earlier her father had died of a heart attack and she still had not fully come to terms with his death. The pain reminded her of her father's death and also connected her to him through the similarity of the site of their troubles.

Whenever Anna's anxiety levels got out of hand, constricting the muscles between her ribs, she panicked and convinced herself that she was suffering from angina and was about to expire. Her hypochondriacal tendencies probably served as a means for containing her generalized anxiety. She refused to do any exercises to improve her muscle tone, which limited the ability of Arsenicum to relieve the muscle spasm around the shoulder area which was causing tension and pain in the rib-cage. In many people this type of pain is easily alleviated by regular exercise such as swimming.

One of the things about the Arsenicum pattern of anxiety is that it is very difficult for the sufferer to see the psychosomatic connections between symptoms and attitudes. The label 'psychosomatic' has been overused and abused, as an almost dismissive way of saying there is nothing wrong with someone. In fact, it points to the indivisible relationship between mind and body, which are on one continuum and cannot be treated separately. If your body is troubling you, you will also be troubled in mind, unless you're suffering from something simple such as a mild infection. So although the fears of someone in an Arsenicum energy pattern may not be proportionate to the level of risk they are facing, these fears are nevertheless real, as they reflect a real disturbance in that person's energy body. These concerns can be very debilitating to those who suffer them.

A fear of not being in control is a big issue for Arsenicum types, and they are very averse to taking risks. They certainly will not bungee jump, unless they decide masochistically to force themselves to face their fears. Paranoid feelings can become extremely limiting. One woman told me that since she had become a mother she was a very nervous driver, and she would never allow all the children to be in the car at one time, in case something happened. While sufferers may be aware of how neurotic these anxieties are, it is difficult to change them consciously while stuck in this energy pattern.

At the bottom of a number of fears is the fear of death. This makes Arsenicum types poor travellers who panic on planes, particularly at take-off and landing. A fear of accidents may lead them to choose to be passengers rather than drive themselves. Yet they are often nervous passengers, trying to relieve their anxious feelings by behaving as back-seat drivers. Those who continue to drive hate to do so in situations they perceive as dangerous, like on motorways or after dark. A fear of train breakdowns means they are unwilling to use this mode of transportation either.

I have treated many women around the menopause who have developed this sort of anxiety, and their lives have become very circumscribed by their dependence on their partner to ferry them around. It has coincided with their children moving out and moving on, leaving them to face the consequent emptiness in their lives. Instead of being able to welcome the new openness in their lives and fill it with things that give them pleasure, women stuck in the Arsenicum energy pattern react by becoming even more fearful and limiting their lives even more than they did when their main concerns and worries were for their children.

Such anxieties can become quite compulsive. A fear of not being able to escape from a theatre or cinema means they can only sit by an exit, or else they prefer not to go at all. A conviction that they have left the gas on can even prevent them from leaving the house, at least until they have made repeated checks. Sometimes they suffer from a phobia about germs, leading to much hand-washing and cleaning. They can be quite obsessional about tidiness, finding it difficult to tolerate disorder. They cannot sit down if anything is out of place in a room. This need to keep their living space spotlessly clean and tidy comes from a deep need to control their environment as a way of staving off the possibility that things could become random and disorderly.

At some point in their lives they have experienced the world as a hostile place, and that is how they still see the world, deep down. It is therefore difficult for them to allow joy in, because hot on the heels of that emotion can come an anxiety about it being taken away. It can be difficult to let go and have an orgasm, for example.

Existence for these people becomes hard, a bit of a grind, even though they are usually high achievers in whatever they do. The quality of being driven means that they are very conscientious, paying attention to detail, and others benefit from their consumate self-control and ability to control situations. But it is hard for them to reap the rewards of their efforts, since they are permanently engaged in forestalling problems. They are chronic worriers, finding problems where there are none. Their anxieties become so habitual that it is difficult for them to think in any different way.

Melanie consulted me due to menstrual difficulties a year after the birth of her son. She complained of swollen breasts, depression and pre-menstrual tension. Anger and upset were compounding her chronic state of exhaustion. It became clear that anxiety was a major indicator of her energy disturbance, since things had begun to go badly after the cot death of a friend's baby, which made her very anxious for her own child. Sex was still uncomfortable, which she put down to the fact that her baby had been induced, making the labour too fast, and the placenta had to be pulled out by hand after the umbilical cord broke.

As we talked more, it emerged that Melanie was also extremely worried about her parents' health. Her mother had high blood pressure and very weak bones as a result of osteoporosis, and her father had developed late-onset diabetes and was very ill. The nervous toll of Melanie's levels of anxiety was apparent in her rapid blinking and frequent bouts of diarrhoea. The constant stress in her life built up so that she regularly suffered from stress symptoms such as exhaustion, insomnia, PMT, allergies, severe colds, sore throats, ulcers, gastritis, diarrhoea, skin eruptions and a frozen shoulder. She was chronically anxious with panic disorder and depression about her life.

Like many people with the Arsenicum energy pattern, Melanie could not travel on trains and was unable to relax at the theatre unless she was sitting near an exit. She explained that she had experienced a loss of confidence and felt fractured. 'It's as if I've lost my centre. I want to be off on my own. I can't let my husband come near me.' In spite of this, Melanie felt resentful that people could not reach her. She said, 'I want to be warm and still, but I feel very negative and angry. I can't stop worrying about the baby, my work, about my daughter's school, and about my husband's work.'

Once Melanie had taken the first dose of her constitutional remedy, Arsenicum, there was an immediate improvement in her anxiety, depression and PMT. When the depression came back some years later, after a series of infections, which were due to overworking and juggling mothering with her work, another dose of Arsenicum produced a similarly dramatic improvement. Over the years, as her parents' health deteriorated, she needed regular repeat doses of the remedy to improve her psychological and physical problems. Her anxiety about her parents reached dramatic levels when her father began to exhibit signs of senility and her mother's health spiralled downwards. Melanie started to worry about her own health, particularly the possibility of inheriting her mother's severe osteoporosis and heart problems and her father's senility.Her chronic anxiety would flare up around visits to one or other of her ailing parents, or when dealing with consultants, paramedics and carers, as well as whenever she had to handle conflict in the relationships among her siblings, who expressed their grief and frustration in different ways. Then she had to deal with the inevitable nursing home and closing up of her parents' marital home.

All of this peaked when Melanie's mother died after a stroke. Her father was unable to take it in, repeatedly asking where his wife was. Melanie was tremendously sad and suffered from outbursts of sobbing, saying that she could not survive such emotional anguish. Once again she became very anxious about her own death, and guiltily worried that she did not retain an awareness of her mother's presence since she had died. She felt completely abandoned.

When Melanie next came to see me she had developed a frozen shoulder as a result of all the stress. It had been immobilized for several months, which made her feel more tired and irritable. Physiotherapy had only aggravated it, and in the end an osteopath suggested ice packs to relieve the inflammation. Again the Arsenicum had a dramatic effect, rebalancing her mental state and physical symptoms. Finding complementary methods to speed the healing of the frozen shoulder was helpful because it made her prioritize ways of managing the high levels of stress in her life. She took up yoga and swimming.

As she explained to me, the death of a parent is an experience you never recover from, in the sense that you are always aware of a gap in your life. The process of recovery entails transforming the experience from an agonizingly raw wound to a bittersweet awareness of love. The stumbling block is often the hardship of seeing your parents deteriorate, and needing to make fraught decisions about their medical care and living arrangements.

For Melanie, the fear of losing her mental faculties and going through the humiliating degradation she had witnessed in her parents was exacerbated by her need to always be in control. Arsenicum loosens the need for those in the Arsenicum pattern to maintain control at all costs, and in Melanie's case enabled her to accept the impossibility of pre-empting this contingency. It diminished the agitation produced by fear, and gave her access to the energy that was normally locked up in fearfulness. Melanie could enjoy and appreciate her own loving family once again, as well as her relationships with her siblings.

What to Expect as the Remedy Works

Taking Arsenicum usually gives prompt relief of any physical symptoms which are somatic expressions of your psychological distress. It breaks the debilitating hold of repetitive bouts of illness. Whenever you are feeling fraught, the remedy relaxes you and stabilizes your energy levels. Instead of feeling restless, frenetic or driven, you feel lass anxious about possible negative outcomes. It reduces the level of free-floating anxiety in those who are chronic 'worriers'.

Arsenicum allows you to let go of the need to be in control. Your mental acuity becomes focused on positive development rather then neurotic self-concern. It reduces your anxiety about people close to you, allowing you to express your care for them in a more constructive way. People who require Arsenicum are usually tremendously competent, effective, conscientious and self-reliant, and can also motivate others. Arsenicum allows this dynamism to be harnessed to a clear sense of purpose and vision; the results can then be astounding. The core knot in the energy pattern of this remedy is one of fear. You try to control things in order to prevent things happening that you are afraid of. The remedy helps you let go of the fear that chaos will ensue if you stopped trying to control everything in your life.

Soul Learning for Arsenicum Album

You need to learn to let go and trust your ability to look after yourself. Allow yourself to experience that the world is not a hostile place, but one of safety.

Aurum Metallicum

The key aspect of the Aurum energy pattern is one of conscientiousness. This sense of duty can become such a yoke that the person affected develops a state of deep depression, feeling that life is a joyless burden and there is no alternative but to continue on in a state of drudgery. The depression can become so deep that they develop a brooding state, which is so heavy at times that they feel suicidal and are weighed down with a mass of dark and foreboding thoughts.

People with the Aurum energy pattern take loss badly, becoming withdrawn, introverted and hopeless. They tend to allow themselves only one close relationship, and when that relationship ends, whether with a parent or life partner, they are unable to remain open emotionally. They feel closed off to the possibility of loving someone else.

Aurum personalities are too serious and conscientious. For instance, they are extremely responsible about their family. The downside of this is that they are unable to delegate. They cannot allow anyone else to look after the needs of their family, because they feel someone else wouldn't do it as well.

They lack a spirit of play and spontaneity. The loss of a sense of humour means that they are unable to relate easily to others. New age teacher Ram Dass talks about needing to get beyond our sense of self – the awareness of our own importance, our personalities, our neuroses – and this is precisely what people with the Aurum energy pattern need to do.

People stuck in an Aurum pattern take themselves too seriously, and sometimes are aloof with others because of their keen intelligence. The price of this over-critical assessment of others' flaws is feeling cut off. They are acutely aware of feeling alienated from the people around them yet don't know how to break the impasse and reach out. Their apparent emotional coldness makes other people ignore their tentative overtures of friendship, which exacerbates their inner state of alienation and can make it very difficult for Aurum people to develop warm, intimate relationships.

They feel that their own needs will not be met in life, but instead of becoming demanding, they concentrate on meeting the needs of others. They may feel that others are unable to see who they really are inside and respond warmly. They feel sad and disappointed, and their expectations of emotional fulfilment diminish the longer they are stuck in this energy pattern.

Aurum people are perceptive: they tend to observe matters closely and make accurate evaluations. They start life with a basic attitude of optimism and high expectations, but they are easily disillusioned because of their emotional sensitivity. Like people stuck in the energy patterns of Ignatia, Silica and Causticum, they suffer when their idealistic aspirations are thwarted. In this particular pattern they respond by becoming hopeless and gloomy, entering into a chronic state of deep depression. A number of people with clinical depression have this energy pattern and respond well to this remedy.

These people internalize a sense of powerlessness, and their sense of foreboding is particularly bad around financial affairs. They react badly to any downturns in the stock market if they have been investing in stocks and shares, for instance. Californians call this tendency to over-react to financial problems 'poverty consciousness'.

The remedy is actually made from the precious metal gold, and people in this energy pattern often feel at some level that their value is linked to that of the financial world.

Tariq wanted treatment because he was suffering from severe hay fever, which had developed when he first arrived in England from Uganda as a boy. When he first came to see me he was working as a civil servant, but in his spare time he tried to express his creativity by writing a Kafkaesque novel which featured himself as the anonymous hero. He was always doing things for other people: it seemed that no effort was too great, yet he did not feel that others reciprocated his consideration of them.

His relationships were turbulent, and his marriage had not worked out. His parents were unhappy that he had rejected the offer of an arranged marriage, but he remained close to his mother, moving house to just around the corner from her once his marriage had broken down.

Tariq felt a deep dissatisfaction with his life and, to dull his feelings, he drank so heavily at times that he eventually collapsed with acute pancreatitis. Alcohol emphasized his darker side, making him more depressed and insular. Sometimes he would just get in his car and drive out into the countryside for some solitude; at other times, when the despair was all-pervasive, he had the urge to press his foot on the accelerator and drive straight into a brick wall. He had a recurrent fantasy of putting his hand through a glass window, an image that reflected the self-destructive way he turned his frustration inwards.

He responded extremely well to Aurum metallicum. Once every year or two he called me, saying his old feelings of frustration and depression were threatening to erupt into self-destructive behaviour again, and that he needed another dose of his remedy. Every time he took it, his deep feeling of depression would lift. No longer feeling hopeless and helpless, he could move forward in his life again. He now cares for his ailing mother.

Tariq's path to healing involved becoming celibate for several years, avoiding relationships until he felt he had cleared out enough of his past troubles not to repeat the problems he had had in previous relationships. He completely abstained from alcohol and drugs and started to meditate. This helped him to ground, open up energetically and connect with others. He discovered that he had an aptitude for healing. He trained as a healer, and is now teaching healing to others.

In the past he experienced a constant debate about his need to change his life. He felt that sitting around drinking was self-indulgent, and was aware that slumming it in bars in rough areas was an insult to the people living there who didn't have the money for a comfortable lifestyle. The first step in changing was to admit to himself that he needed help, and come for treatment. Through his journey toward healing, Tariq has realized that his 'weakness' – always putting others' needs first – was part of a need to help others. He has always been on the path of service, but is now conscious of it.

What to Expect as the Remedy Works

Taking Aurum clears up cases of deep depression. If it is the correct remedy for you, you no longer feel suicidal because the remedy helps you to align yourself with the vitality of life. It allows you to regain your *joie de vivre* and learn to play again. You will find that you enjoy life once again and do things from a sense of pleasure rather than dutiful responsibility. You re-discover the excitement of engaging in the world that you lost sight of somewhere along the way. You learn to stop nurturing others at the expense of nurturing yourself; it's necessary to look after your own emotional and spiritual needs to avoid 'burning out'. You stop thinking that you are the only one who can care for your loved ones properly, and learn to allow others to share the burden. By being less dutiful, you open yourself to much more love than you may have experienced before.

Soul Learning for Aurum

Learning that the universe is love, and that you can share in this loving experience.

Calcarea Carbonica

The key issue for people in the energy pattern of this remedy is to do with willpower. They do have the will to do things but not much stamina, so it can be difficult for them to persevere. If things do not go easily, they tend to give up. This happened on a profound level to Raphael, whose daughter became schizophrenic after her husband left her the day after their son was born. Raphael felt a failure as a parent, and that his failings as a parent may have contributed to his daughter's inability to cope. On a deep level that was difficult to acknowledge, he felt a sense of regret that he had ever had children. He was afflicted with a profound depression while struggling to respond helpfully to the situation, and needed Calcarea carbonica to hep him regain his strength of resolve.

People stuck in this energy pattern can suffer from a lack of self-assertion. In this state, they are afraid that someone will see through them and perceive a lack of substance in them. But one woman described how her preoccupation with her children and her obstinate character proved to be strengths in pursuing her vision of excellence in state education. She ended up successfully running an influential company producing education materials.

People with the Calcarea pattern also have a sense of emotional neediness, which makes them want to please others so that others will want to spend time with them. They lack the confidence to branch out alone, to take risks, to build new relationships. They may want things to be handed to them on a plate, without having to struggle for them. Their passivity can lead to a victim mentality and a tendency to give up and give in. They collapse into depression when significant relationships end or their home breaks up. Family life is important to them because they identify themselves as on the path of home-making. They are domesticated, enjoying making a welcoming home and preparing family dinners. They feel fulfilled when everyone is gathered around the table at meal-times.

The positive soul properties of this remedy pattern include openness and an awareness of the realm of spirit. Their passivity in life can allow them to be less controlling of their destiny, and thus more in harmony with the events that are happening around them. They are attracted to a spiritual perspective and feel motivated when imbued with a sense of faith which can provide them with much-needed support. One woman with the Calcarea carbonica pattern described her involvement in her religious community as an extension of her involvement in and support of her family.

People with this pattern sometimes struggle with feelings of lassitude, apathy and a lack of motivation. If this is the case, they want to sleep a lot, and while they sleep the world passes them by. They feel hampered by inertia and a lack of will to do things. They do have energy when there are other people around, but find it very difficult to motivate themselves when alone. They have a range of physical problems caused by a sluggish metabolism. They can suffer from poor elimination, which causes constipation, a lot of sweating, and spotty skin. They tend to crave exactly those kinds of foods that do not suit their metabolism, preferring carbohydrates, fatty and sugary foods. Such a diet, coupled with a lack of exercise, can lead to poor circulation and fatigue. People with this energy pattern may also have problems with an underactive thyroid gland.

Cynthia felt increasingly sluggish after turning 40. She was chilly and putting on weight – signs that her metabolism was slowing down. Women around this age are particularly prone to thyroid imbalance: in this case the problem was under-functioning, in which the digestion slows down, causing low energy and poor elimination. Her legs became very swollen in the summer heat and were full of cellulite. Her brain seemed foggy, and she could not remember how to spell things. When her partner talked to her, she found it difficult to concentrate.

'I live in permanent hiding within myself, hence the short-sightedness, the lack of memory and of ambition, the lack of substance. Yet sometimes there's a revolt in me, when I glimpse the possibilities, the time wasted, the pain and the injustice. I've been dogged for years by a black cloud, feeling depressed for no apparent reason and crying.'

Cynthia often felt sad and lonely, and when she was like this for some time she would go into a deep depression. It was a feeling of not wanting to go on, when her life felt pointless; she described it as a fear of being alive. She said, 'I keep apologizing for my existence.' She felt powerless when her son was beaten up in a nightclub, crying because she 'didn't understand the need for such violence and hatred in the world'. It made her feel hopeless and she said that she had wanted to die.

After years of psychotherapy, Cynthia was still trying to heal her feelings of abandonment by her father and her violent mother. Her father had left the family when she was 10 and never got in touch again. She was emotionally sensitive and her moods oscillated. She felt taken for granted in her relationship. She would become vulnerable, weepy, silent and withdrawn, so that she pushed her partner away. At other times she would get very angry, shouting at her teenage children and throwing things around. She felt she had done enough for her children, and did not want to give any more. 'I've done all that for years.' She felt she was doing things because she ought to, without any real enthusiasm.

After she had taken Calcarea carbonica, Cynthia became more aware of the situations that made her angry. She realized that her reactions occurred whenever she felt passed over or left out. She noticed that her anger towards her partner was more to do with her own failure to make more of her life and took more responsibility for her own problems. Then she acknowledged how angry she was at her sister, who had always been envious of her and made her feel guilty. She responded by writing a letter to her mother in which she tried to express her deep feelings for the first time in years. Although her mother didn't respond to her letters, Cynthia felt much less despairing.

Depression is often connected with unexpressed anger, and once a person finds a constructive way to vent it, the feelings of impotence and depression are relieved.

Cynthia went on to feel more positive and confident, and began taking driving lessons. She had been anxious about driving for years. Passing her test was an important step in becoming more independent, and helped create opportunities for her to pursue her own interests. Her partner bought her a car, which made her feel supported in her efforts to get 'back in the driving seat' of her life, and less resentful towards him as she found herself becoming less dependent on him.

What to Expect as the Remedy Works

After taking Calcarea carbonica your problems of inertia and energetic stasis start to improve and you become more energized. You no longer feel worn out physically and emotionally. You feel more resilient than before and can respond to life events in a more adaptable manner. You become patient and accept the pace of your own energy flow, which can be slower than for those with a fast metabolic rate. Slow and systematic progress will get you to your goal in the end.

Calcarea helps you become more clear mentally, so you can let go of the small insecurities that have stopped you focusing on what is really important. As you feel more confident, you can be more effective. You feel motivated again on an emotional level and experience greater closeness with your loved ones. You enjoy your domestic role again, and regain your appetite for good food along with your lust for life. Your desire to make everything safe and cozy for others is laudable, but this remedy helps you appreciate the fact that you do not have to strive all the time to accomplish this. You do not need to try so hard to make it all right for everyone. You can trust that things will not fall apart if you have not done everything you intended to do.

Soul Learning of Calcarea Carbonica

You need to trust that, if you hold on to your vision, you will achieve your goal.

Causticum

People in the Causticum remedy pattern are motivated by an idealistic vision that arises from a deep sense of empathy. From an early age they have a tendency to experience the suffering of others as if it were their own. It is this altruistic empathy that orients them on a path of service. They have an intellectual approach to understanding the world, and with their sophisticated political awareness, they often become politically involved as a means of furthering social change.

The typical energy block of this remedy pattern arises when this idealism becomes frustrated, whether because of ineptitude within a group or organization, or legal and political impediments from outside. In this situation, people with the Causticum pattern can become irritable and impatient, with a need to control others. Their drive for justice can make them confrontational and indignant, so that they may be unable to deal with institutions or authority in a productive way. Their need to be in the right may leave them in a stance of always fighting against authority, so that their energy is literally frustrated. They tend to internalize a lot of suppressed anger. On a physical level, they can suffer a chronic sense of apprehensive anxiety in their abdomen, which is where the energy seems to become blocked within their bodies. As a result, they develop stress-related conditions such as eczema, anal fissures, fibrocitis or compulsive checking syndromes.

People in the energy pattern of this remedy often try to suppress their spiritual inclinations because of an abhorrence of the abuses of power by those in whom religious authority is vested by society. One woman who came to me could not acknowledge her religious feelings because they did not fit in with the identity she had constructed for herself as a politically motivated lesbian feminist. We discussed her need to reconcile the side of herself that she had cut off for many years. The background yearning had never quite left her awareness. She decided to see a woman priest and began a series of meetings to discuss the difficulty of reconciling her adolescent faith with her current rationalist world view. She struggled with feelings of embarrassment doing this, but she knew she had to allow herself to explore her spiritual feelings, which had never gone away, despite her cynical stance.

Grace was a 36-year-old lawyer married to a social worker. Her husband was ready for them to have children, but she was ambivalent because she could not see how he could cut back on his work to help care for them.

Her metabolism was generally sluggish. Grace felt chilly and suffered from poor circulation. She got constipated if she ate much meat, and she had put on weight.

She had stopped taking the contraceptive pill in order to try and improve her health and to find out if her menstrual cycle would re-establish itself without problems. She didn't know whether taking the pill for 17 years had affected her fertility. When she discontinued it, the facial acne she used to suffer from as a teenager recurred. Her sex drive had been chronically low, but became a little better after she stopped taking the pill. The couple found a few sessions of sex therapy helpful; the therapist identified their fundamental problem as needing to prioritize spending time together. Sharing quality time is essential in order to develop greater intimacy.

Grace was very committed to her work. The things she felt powerless to change gripped her with acute anxiety in the abdominal area called the solar plexus. This was sometimes caused by things that frustrated her personally, and sometimes by clients' trampled rights, which she felt indignant about. She had always been idealistic, going into law because she wanted to be an agent for social change.

Early in life Grace had developed an acute awareness of women's inequality. Even as a child she was driven to prove that she was as good as – or better than – boys. The only daughter in a large family, she played rugby and soccer hard, and could score goals better than her brothers. She saw her father as a dominating patriarch and her mother as a downtrodden victim, and had always been concerned not to allow herself to get into that position of powerlessness. Grace had determined that she would never be dependent on a man, hence her deep-seated reluctance to becoming a mother. Her own mother had always said she could not leave her father 'because of the children'.

Grace spent years working in the field of family law, but became demoralized dealing with endless custody battles and cases of child abuse. In spite of her passionate motivation, she was ambivalent about working in law almost from the beginning, since getting picky about detail could make one lose sight of the broader issues. Her own approach was to try and understand the ways people had been mistreated or taken advantage of, penetrating to the heart of the matter in order to work out the best method of approaching the case. Her empathic nature meant that she tended to get over-involved in her clients' problems, almost making them personal issues.

After taking Causticum, Grace was absolutely exhausted for a couple of days. The remedy showed her true energy levels: that is, how little energy she had when she was not mustering the adrenaline she needed to keep going. By the end of a week, her energy improved and became more balanced.

With her homeopathic treatment, Grace started on a path that involved reconciling her righteous anger towards her mother for being a victim. This needed to be healed before she could make her own journey into motherhood. When she did get pregnant, she arranged for a locum to take over her job and took a year off work. Her friends seemed amazed that she expected her husband to change from being a workaholic, but as she said, 'I don't take things lying down.' During the pregnancy, she became even more adversarial and sensitive to the issue of injustice, but this no longer caused her such stress.

What to Expect as the Remedy Works

Causticum helps you not to take social problems so personally. It clears up any physical symptoms that are related to your frustration at the injustices you observe around you. It enables you to take a more gentle stance in facilitating social change, without being any less effective. You have more internal resources to find a way of harnessing your idealism to make your vision manifest.

Taking the remedy helps you to deal with disillusionment by letting go of fixed ideas or rigid attachments to particular goals. It widens your sense of perspective to include the soul as well as the social dimension. You realize that you do not always have to fight against institutions that attempt to claim authority over your experience. On a spiritual level, you see that you do not have to accept the institutional structures or the whole package of dogma that surrounds any particular faith. In this way, taking Causticum helps you reconcile your political vision with a spiritual awareness and deepens your commitment to the path of service.

Soul Learning for Causticum

Accepting the authority of your own inner experience.

Ignatia

The central theme of the Ignatia energy pattern is the effect on the emotions of dealing with disappointment. This remedy is well known as a treatment for grief (see page 130) because its pattern corresponds to a state of emotional and physical contraction in the face of loss. Ignatia enlivens the numbed state that develops straight after the death or loss of someone we care about. In this state of shock there is a physical seizing up as well, where the person feels they cannot breathe deeply, or that they cannot swallow properly. In this context, the sensation of a lump in the throat is associated with unexpressed tears.

People in an Ignatia energy pattern experience tremendous grief at the end of relationships with people who were never or rarely fully present emotionally. For example, grief may be caused by the loss of a parent to whom the person was never really close. It may be intense at the end of a love affair that was never consummated sexually, or by the emotional turmoil of getting over-involved with a lover who is married to someone else. This energy pattern is often present in people who struggle to get close to partners who are scared of commitment and who are forever prevaricating about being in the relationship.

The sense of unfulfilled hopes, dashed dreams and disappointed love creates a feeling of hopelessness. This is not the dreadful despair found in the Aurum metallicum state (see page 180); at times it is almost a nostalgic mood. Nevertheless, it is an intense feeling that leaves people in the Ignatia pattern sighing and wringing their hands. In some people this kind of disappointment is a repeated pattern, following each and every let-down. They can be in this state for months, and it feels very intense until it suddenly lifts, which is usually when they find another object for their desires.

This remedy pattern is associated with what happens when people withdraw their loving feelings altogether when the person they loved is no longer there to reciprocate. If their love was exclusively directed at a single person rather than being expansive and all-inclusive, they may feel they have no more love to give. The risk of reacting in this way is that their life becomes a source of disappointment. This disappointment is to do with the hopes and fantasies they once had which have never been fulfilled. It is also to do with the opportunities they think they have missed, and emotional 'business' which they feel is unfinished.

People in the Ignatia pattern project their needs onto the people they love. Even after a relationship has broken down, they continue to fantasize about what might be; they prefer to stay in this state of fantasy rather than risk getting hurt again in another relationship. They have a generally romantic disposition with idealistic expectations about relationships. It can be difficult to accept that they're responsible for meeting their own emotional needs and shaping their own lives.

They are emotionally volatile, sympathetic and responsive to the needs of others. Altruistic, they will often put a lot of energy into worthwhile causes. They are spiritually evolved, yet run into problems when others don't treat them with consideration and sensitivity. They can react in perverse ways; for instance by denying their feelings, then bursting out with tempestuous emotions.

Nancy was a 32-year-old financial advisor who had suffered from clinical depression over the previous two years. Her counsellor felt that she was not making headway and recommended the anti-depressant, Prozac, which she was reluctant to take. At the start of this trouble, her metabolism had slowed down and her thyroid was found to be under-functioning, but in spite of taking hormonal supplements there had been no improvement in her general condition. At the time she consulted me, Nancy was also taking steroid inhalers for asthma; this was a long-term problem she had suffered from since childhood.

She felt very bleak. There was no joy in her life, and she did not want to go out of her flat after work. She experienced the world as an evil place and said that she just did not feel right in it. 'After Mum died I felt I let go of everything – I was close to her. I'd washed my hands of everything and I had to start all over again with my life. I felt anesthetized and stopped crying.'

When Nancy was born her mother was 45. During Nancy's youth her mother had been ill with heart failure, and then died shortly after Nancy moved to London for a relationship that did not work out. On top of all this, Nancy's housing situation became critical and she ended up camping on a friend's floor for several months. She started to wake regularly at 3 a.m., feeling desolate and crying. She kept tormenting herself with questions as to why the relationship with her boyfriend had not worked and imagined constantly how things could have been. 'He said he didn't love me. I never spoke to him again after that, but I often felt his presence – sometimes I felt as if he was in bed beside me.'

All her upset was focused on this man. Nancy was always dwelling on what might have been, ignoring the fact that he actually did not love her and had told her so, and therefore none of what she fantasized for the relationship could ever have been possible. She also felt hopeless about ever meeting a new partner and starting a family. Because of what had happened, she felt totally let down by men and disappointed in them. She had no expectation of anything good happening in the future.

Directly after taking Ignatia, Nancy described an unusual experience of feeling full of love for everyone. The sound of her voice was lighter and brighter, and friends commented that she seemed happier. The periods of hopelessness became less frequent, and her negative thoughts eased up. Her ability to concentrate gradually improved and the headaches she had been suffering from cleared up. She felt mentally sharper and was more efficient at work, but she was still very unhappy with her job and living situation, and was plagued by regrets about the man who had let her down.

Ignatia cleared Nancy's pointless preoccupation with her ex. It stopped her missing him and fantasizing about how things could have been. People stuck in the energy pattern of this remedy usually get hooked on someone unavailable, and in Nancy's case the man she loved was not available because he did not want her. Emotions flared up in her once again when she passed him in the street, but she was able to let go of her hopelessness after a couple of days. Whole days passed without her crying, because she was no longer obsessively focusing on her lack of a relationship.

A couple of months after she took the first dose of Ignatia, the remnants of Nancy's depression lifted completely. She found herself more engaged in what was going on in her life in the present, instead of being obsessively stuck in the past. She stopped feeling passive and hopeless about her situation and she got more insights out of going to counselling. She also started to attend some night classes. She found she was able to sleep through the night again.

However, her path to healing was not smooth. Powerful and upsetting images recurred in her dreams. In one, for instance, she dreamed she was being pursued by a maniac and could not manage to make contact with the police. In another dream, someone was trying to saw her into bits. These themes were a sign of her deep fears and anxieties, now manifesting themselves in her dreams rather than in anxious bouts of insomnia.

As Nancy's emotions were released from the past, she began to cry more. After taking this remedy it is quite common for frozen feelings to start thawing and for strong emotions to start coming out. The person experiences relief after a good cry.

Nancy then went through a stage of emotional crisis in which she felt very overwhelmed by her feelings and even had a panic attack with hyperventilation. Although it was frightening at the time, she found it a turning point in her life. It prompted her to re-evaluate the things that were making her anxious and pushed her to resign from her job, which had been causing a lot of dissatisfaction. This turnaround was also marked by a flurry of constructive activity in which Nancy changed her living situation: she applied for jobs, found a better house to live in, and even went to a friend's wedding. It no longer seemed so impossible to pursue the possibility of romantic love. She stopped feeling so down about herself and her appearance.

Instead of trying to control everything, and especially relationships that might be potentially disappointing or hurtful, Nancy described herself as 'going with the flow' as a result of the homeopathic treatment. This helped her in choosing a new flat-share and job.

She came off the steroid drug Becotide without her asthma flaring up. She coped with episodes of tightness in her chest by using breathing techniques that she learned on a yoga therapy course. She even went mountain climbing without any problems.

The anniversary of her mother's death came round again, and Nancy found it much more bearable than in previous years. She decided to attempt to bridge the gap with her estranged father by going to see him. Overall, she had much more energy. She felt more positive about herself than she had for years, and she was full of ideas about different career possibilities that would mean completely new directions.

What to Expect as the Remedy Works

If Ignatia is the right remedy for you, taking it will help you to overcome your disappointment, whether in romantic relationships or life situations. It calms you when you are overwrought, and clears up symptoms associated with grief, such as insomnia, or an inability to swallow because of the sensation of a lump in the throat. If you haven't expressed your emotional distress through talking about what has happened and crying, taking Ignatia will often bring tears to the surface, or a series of healing dreams.

Ignatia will heal your grief and disappointment. If you have high expectations it will help you accept the inevitable shortfall. If you have strong passions, it will restore equilibrium. If you project your fantasies onto a person you cannot build a committed relationship with, it encourages you to drop those fantasies and start looking at how to fulfil your own ideals. When your internal balance has been restored you can start to experience love as a universal energy which is always available for you. How you choose to direct the love you discover within you is then up to you.

Soul Learning for Ignatia

It is up to you to fulfil your own expectations. Try seeing your grief as an opportunity to heal the disappointments you have gone through in life.

Lachesis

The central theme of the Lachesis energy pattern is one of competition. For people in this pattern, competitiveness is tied up with a feeling of having to prove themselves in the world. Instead of fully experiencing their path as their own and appreciating its uniqueness, they are always keeping an eye on how others are doing and evaluating them favourably or unfavourably. When they believe that what they are achieving compares favourably with someone else, they feel a kind of superiority which makes them behave benevolently towards that person. But if their luck changes and the other person starts doing better, it suddenly becomes apparent to everyone that it has been a race all along. This can come as a great surprise to the other person, who may be a close friend. It can even surprise the Lachesis people themselves.

Lachesis personalities are go-getting: they throw themselves into life and try to squeeze as much out of every experience as possible. However, this can leave them prone to feeling that the intensity of experience which they crave is not met in their own life. They may feel that other people's lives are delivering more intensity than theirs is. In order to assuage an underlying fear of inadequacy, they can develop an over-bearing aura of omnipotence. They need to feel they are pivotal in the lives of others, and can behave in demanding, controlling or manipulative ways in an effort to attract maximum attention. When they talk about other people, their main concern is not for their welfare, but for their own reflected glory.

People needing Lachesis are prone to envy. Being self-aware, they may become acutely uncomfortable at observing their envy; but this does not, however, help them combat these feelings. When they can no longer contain envious urges, they often slip into behaviour that they know is immature and misjudged. Emotional outbursts can blow up suddenly, in which they become demanding or aggressive towards others. There are occasions when they refuse to share their own good fortune with friends, or when they do not pass on information that they know others would benefit from. Sometimes they find themselves running a friend down to a third party. At other times they find themselves actively trying to trip the other person up, or secretly gloating over some misfortune of theirs.

This behaviour is all caused by the fact that when someone else is doing well, Lachesis people feel that they have been made smaller by that success. Conversely, when someone else is doing badly, they feel better. These reactions are part of an egotistical, self-centred view that needs always to put the self at the centre of attention. The bluff and bluster of this egotism hides a demanding, childish part inside, and when feelings get heated, tantrums and scenes often arise. People with the Lachesis energy pattern find it difficult to change how they behave, even when they know their behaviour is childish. At the time it is happening, they just do not care how they appear to other people.

Those whose pattern corresponds to Lachesis are also prone to sexual jealousy. They need to fascinate others, especially sexually, and hate to think someone else might be more attractive. One woman said she always felt jealous when her lover paid more attention to friends than to her. 'I know it's wrong,' she said, 'but I feel like screaming "what about me?" like a five-year-old throwing a tantrum.' When there is cause for feeling betrayed, they will create a scene in public, or cut up their lover's clothes. In fact they will do anything rather than

remedies for the soul

talk things over or try to look at how the situation arose and what might need to be done. More often than not there is no cause for this jealousy, but those who require this remedy feel possessive and suspicious of imagined infidelities. Their feelings are intense, and they can suffer from high blood pressure. Luckily their hypertension responds well to this remedy.

People in this energy pattern have a strong sexual nature, but there is often an internal battle going on between their hedonism and moral side, which they sometimes put down to their commitment to spiritual growth. Because of their poor impulse control, they feel their hedonistic side lets them down and they struggle to integrate these two aspects. They may oscillate between strict self-control and rampant self-indulgence, and may struggle with an attraction to drugs or alcohol.

They have strong emotions and are very attuned to the feelings and motives of others, almost as if they can read their minds. Unfortunately they can attempt to manipulate others in order to get their own way. The need for a dramatic outlet for their feelings is mainly about needing to be the centre of attention. The ego has become inflated somewhere along the way, usually to compensate for insecurity and vulnerability. In fact, the ego has been inflated to such an extent that people with the Lachesis pattern no longer see other people as having the right to an independent existence: all they see in other people is a reflection of what is going on in themselves.

Webster was a college student who resented his tutor for giving him critical feedback. His response was to complain to his classmates and the principal, in an attempt to discredit the tutor. He got what he wanted, which was actually more attention from the tutor and his fellow students. The tutor became cautious in her comments on Webster's work after experiencing such an intensely angry reaction. This served to disguise any deficiencies there may have been in his work, and thus raised his profile at the college.

Like other people who have benefited from the Lachesis remedy, Webster had a strongly developed ego. However, it emerged that his behaviour was erratic. Sometimes he was charming and could not do enough for his friends, at other times he flew into a rage. Whatever his mood, he always behaved in an intense manner with others. He never stopped talking, unless it was to enjoy good food or sex, since he was something of a sensualist. When he wasn't in a sexual relationship, he masturbated several times a day.

He had problems with alcohol, going on a binge every week or two. His irrationally changeable behaviour was typical of those with a borderline personality disorder, which suggested that in fact his sense of self was poorly formed and very fragile. Taking Lachesis stabilized Webster's mood swings and reduced his need to ceaselessly vent his emotions, whether through anger, ejaculation or endless talking. Over a number of years, taking Lachesis was instrumental in solidifying his sense of self and expanding it to encompass an awareness of his interactions with others. He became less self-centred and easier to be around.

What to Expect as the Remedy Works

Lachesis resolves the feeling of inadequacy, envy and competitiveness which underlie jealousy. If you are in this energy pattern, you have a lot of energy but you expend much of it on maintaining an inflated sense of self. What Lachesis will do for you is to transform this energy, allowing it to change and flow in more productive directions. You are more capable in your working life. You are more able to complete creative projects. As a result of angsting less about sex, your intimate relationships become easier. You appreciate what you get from others, rather than getting trapped in envy. You feel less driven and are able to relax more.

The remedy improves any gynaecological or sexual problems you have had, when your blocked sexual energy is released. When sexual energy flows more smoothly you feel satisfied and more magnanimous toward others than before. Lachesis reconnects your sexuality with your heart. It helps you redefine yourself in an expanded self that encompasses your sexual and spiritual sides.

Soul Learning for Lachesis

You have a strong drive towards both the spiritual and the sexual. You need to integrate these two poles of yourself so that you have a whole sexuality. The way to do this is to reconnect your sexuality with your heart and your soul.

Lycopodium

The central theme of the Lycopodium remedy pattern is a lack of confidence. People in this pattern are sensitive to criticism. Undermining experiences in their lives have dented their confidence, making them retreat into an internal world in which they buffer themselves by throwing themselves into their hobbies or interests. Lycopodium personalities have good mental faculties, so they get involved in literature, art, science or any other intellectual pursuit that is relatively solitary. These are areas in which they can express their emotional sensitivity in 'safety'. However, they can end up feeling isolated because they feel like loners and find it hard to mix socially. They are aware of their isolation, but do not always know how to bridge the gap between themselves and others. Emotional communication is not a strong point with these people. They may be affectionate, but find it challenging to be demonstrative about how they feel.

Their lack of confidence can manifest itself in specific areas of life – most commonly as insecurity in the world of work, while becoming bossy and domineering at home. Their sense of inadequacy is relieved by feeling superior to those further down the pecking order. So the person stuck in the energy pattern of the remedy Lycopodium can come across as very confident, even arrogant and bombastic, with friends and family, while they feel as if they constantly have to prove themselves professionally. Because of this sensitivity they are very aware of the balance of power in any situation, and may feel the need to shore up their own uncertain sense of authority. They spend a lot of time thinking about conflicts that they are embroiled in, and yet they often find it difficult directly to confront situations that are troubling them or to talk about things in an open and honest way.

They fear that opening up about their feelings or acknowledging that they feel slighted in some way will weaken their position vis-à-vis the person with power. They may worry about bringing up their complaints about their work conditions because of a fear of losing their job. Although they like to make themselves appear indispensable, they are dogged by a feeling that, in reality, they are only too dispensable.

These stresses and anxieties can make them irritable. They tend to complain when they feel overburdened with responsibilities and sometimes they try to shirk them. They feel trapped if they have all the financial responsibility for their dependents, and they can be grudging with money as well as with time spent with their families.

Those needing Lycopodium lack confidence in their ability to determine the future, even though they are not lacking in confidence on a day-to-day level. Whatever they do, they do well. Nonetheless, they can spend an unnecessary amount of time worrying about things that, in the end, turn out to be all right. For instance, speaking up in meetings or giving presentations is a particular ordeal for those in the Lycopodium energy pattern. Other situations where people suffer in anticipation of public speaking may respond to the energy patterns of Silica or Arsenicum album.

Kevin, a 50-year-old architect, had been suddenly hit by pneumonia and herpes encephalitis (a condition where a herpes virus inflames the brain tissues) five years before he came to see me. It was taking him years to recover, and he came in complaining that his sense of smell had not come back, although his sense of taste had partially returned. He was troubled by fretful dreams and woke up frequently at night. His sleep had still not settled, his stomach was disturbed, and he felt too exhausted and depressed to work properly. Pain from trapped wind in his abdomen would wake him in the early hours of the morning, especially when he was anxious. He had to sleep propped up because his stomach was so sensitive. His bowels were usually 'seized up' with constipation.

Kevin's health had not been very good even before he contracted the viral infection. For example, he'd had a convulsion and had then been put on anti-convulsant drugs for some time. These had left him with what was called 'mild expressive dysphasia', which meant that his memory for specific words was blocked so that he could not recall people's names or proper nouns. When tired, his thinking became obsessional. Strangely, his normal facility for German (which he'd learned at school) became intrusive, especially when fatigued.

Because of his health problems, Kevin had resigned as a partner in his architecture firm and tried to let go of his ambitions – however, he felt dogged by failure. An earlier marriage had failed, and he was going through a difficult phase with his current wife. He experienced a lot of anticipatory anxiety and was distracted and overwrought, imagining all the things that could go wrong at work. He was fearful of disapproval. He tended to take on what others said about him, feeling that he was no good deep inside. He felt so bad that sometimes he would just sit with his hands over his face, wanting to run away and hide.

Because he was afraid of others' anger, he never recognized it in himself, always thinking anger was someone else's problem. Then he became very angry when his aged mother wanted to remarry shortly after his father's death. He saw this as an Oedipal anger at her new lease of life, because of her intense relationship with him, which he felt had blocked his sexuality right into his thirties, with disastrous consequences for his first marriage.

Kevin's doctor had prescribed the antidepressant Prozac and tried several courses of antibiotics, which seemed to have no effect other than to exacerbate his gastric problems. He complained that Prozac had made him 'spaced out' and did not help his depression; also, it disturbed his sleep even further. He felt that he was not just suffering from depression, but had had a breakdown of sorts. These drugs seemed inadequate to the task of dealing with Kevin's complex problems. By reducing Kevin's physical and psychological symptoms to the label of depression, more fundamental problems that needed sorting out risked being masked by the drug. Soon after starting it, however, Kevin had decided to stop taking the Prozac because he could not cope with what he described as 'living in a hazy reality'.

The remedy Lycopodium worked for Kevin on the many levels that needed rebalancing. It relaxed his bowels, allowing wind to pass and producing softer movements. I also advised him to cut right back on carbohydrates, to put less strain on his digestive system. He noticed that his stomach tended to flare up in direct proportion to his workload. Many people stuck in the energy pattern of this remedy have digestive problems, suffering from bloating, flatulence, constipation and acid indigestion. These are usually signs of a sluggish, overloaded digestive system which needs cleansing.

As well as relieving his physical symptoms, Lycopodium stimulated Kevin's energy and improved his mood. He was able to concentrate at work again and his memory was sharper. His sleep was more refreshing so that he was able to go into work early to clear up some of the back-log that had accumulated.

Lycopodium improved Kevin's confidence so that he was able to see things more realistically – both the demands he made on himself and those made on him by others. Yet he still did not feel that he could let everyone (and himself) down by stopping work. His path to healing involved a long struggle inside himself before he was able to let go of his attachment to his job. He realized that his identity didn't rest on being an architect, and he finally left the firm in order to pursue language studies.

Kevin sought individual and couple counselling to help himself and his wife deal with the buried problems that had created distance, depression and sexual disconnection. He discovered that his sexual functioning was linked to feelings of inadequacy and failure, and that the problem resolved itself once he and his wife were communicating better.

What to Expect as the Remedy Works

If it's the remedy indicated for you, Lycopodium will give you the courage to change the direction of your life. It works slowly but surely. First, it enables you to admit the extent of your dissatisfaction, which is a pre-requisite for taking effective action. It helps you to overcome any fears you may have of public exposure or humiliation. Once you have overcome these fears you will be able to 'stand up and be counted'. You develop the courage of your personal convictions.

Lycopodium helps you feel more confident and secure in your own power. In the past you may not have felt recognized by authority figures in your life, and this feeling of powerlessness made you try to claim some share of power by wielding it over others. Your experience of power was that it was imposed from the outside, which made you believe that the only way to be strong was to strive for power over others. The remedy allows you to step into your own personal power.

The remedy clarifies your will and uncovers your own unique vision. Lycopodium also cleanses your liver, a process that you can help by following a detoxification diet. Your liver is considered the seat of the will; when it is cleansed, you can formulate your intentions more clearly. Your will is the driving force for manifesting your vision in the world.

Soul Learning for Lycopodium

Harnessing your will to the purpose of manifesting your vision in the world. Try to see your intellectual frustrations and feelings of powerlessness as an opportunity to step into your own personal power.

Medorrhinum

Medorrhinum is a high-energy remedy pattern, with a strong desire for sensory stimulation and lots of experiences. Attracted to intensity of all sorts, people with this energy pattern want life to be a high as much as possible. They are impatient, though: they want their highs to be instantly on tap. Therefore, they like to live on the wild side, taking risks in the search for thrills. This desire for stimulation, coupled with an emotional instability, leads to an addictive personality, whether this means addiction to substances such as alcohol or to experiences such as sex.

The search for easy gratification gets in the way of the deeper search for meaning of a lasting kind. Medorrhinum personalities may have trouble distinguishing the real from the fake. Resorting to pharmaceuticals to produce an altered state of consciousness means they can avoid developing the kind of consciousness that is necessary to develop the innate capacities that we all have.

The high of a drug-induced experience is usually followed by the chemical repercussions of the substance – a drug-induced low. People in this remedy pattern tend to swing between extreme states, feeling on top of the world one moment and then miserable the next. This tendency is only aggravated by the taking of illicit drugs.

Addiction shows that the soul is having trouble finding itself. The debate has gone on for a long time about the value of drug-induced altered states of consciousness as a source of religious experience. I believe that drugs can only intensify aspects of ourselves that are already there, aspects which we are not normally conscious of. So unless we work to develop the depth of our inner lives, drugs cannot put us in touch with our souls.

Certain drugs (heroin, crack and cocaine in particular) seem to smash a person's moral fibre, unravelling the values that are expressive of the soul. Without soul qualities such as integrity, the ego gets out of hand, pursuing everything just for itself. Altered states of consciousness become increasingly superficial, sexual experiences increasingly empty, parties increasingly banal. This is because the ego is grasping at these experiences without connecting with other people or with a deeper spiritual reality. Overcoming addiction involves learning integrity, which is usually destroyed in users of hard drugs. In order to let go of an addiction to highs, you need to learn to develop willpower.

Adam, who worked in the leisure industry, had been using alcohol for many years to mask his difficult feelings. He was never happy except when things in his life were intense. At the same time he often felt as if his strong feelings would overwhelm him, and he used drink for many years to keep these emotions at bay. Beneath the surface there was a lot of rage towards his authoritarian father, and about his parents' acrimonious divorce, which had happened just as he was entering adolescence. At the time he had managed to avoid too much flak by being cute whenever attention was on him, while at the same time withdrawing into himself. He became increasingly shy and suffered from feelings of worthlessness.

Because he had become used to controlling his feelings, Adam hived off unacceptable parts of his personality into sub-personalities who popped up in daily life. One character was gruff and bear-like and would go off in a huff if he did not like anything; one was a domineering tyrant; another one was tactically manipulative – for instance, he would get his girlfriend to do the housework by grudgingly offering to do another chore instead.

As an adult, Adam felt unsure of himself and avoided taking responsibility for himself and others. He had been in a relationship for several years but felt he could not make a commitment to his partner. He was constantly wracked by doubts about whether he was in the right relationship, the right job or the right life. He felt very anxious about the way his life seemed to be passing by, yet he could not free himself from his constant internal monologue of doubt and anger.

Adam had been using alcohol to blot out these discontented, doubting voices, and once he did stop drinking he had to deal with the competing drives and dissonant voices that commented on everything he did in his daily life. His alcoholism was a measure of the self-destructiveness he experienced as a result of trying to contain his feelings of rage. Treatment with the remedy Medorrhinum enabled Adam to let go of his need to punish himself and others through irritability, angry outbursts and punitive periods of emotional withdrawal. He was able to explore ways to heal and integrate his sub-personalities. As this healing took place, Adam discovered how these other voices had served to distract him from a monologue of discontent.

Adam found the resources inside himself to keep renewing his commitment to changing his attitude towards his life. Medorrhinum calmed his restless mind and gave him some internal space free from angst. In this space he became more aware of his ability to feel good, although he was still conscious of some resistance to allowing that realization to penetrate fully. Homeopathic remedies can work in ways that are similar to meditation, quieting the busy mind with its intrusive thought processes and negativity.

Over the space of three or four years, Adam became much less driven and anxious. He discovered that, in order to free himself from obsessional questioning, he needed to remain focused on his purpose in life. He learned that he needed to let go of his regrets about the past and the blame he laid on his parents for spoiling his innocence, and he needed to stop worrying about the future. He found that if he concentrated on the present, the future would take care of itself. Maintaining this approach required constant attention, but he felt increasingly at peace with himself and more accepting of life just as it was. He decided to accept his tendency to agonize over things and ignore the dictates of his thoughts, and found that they dropped away when starved of attention.

Finding peace and happiness through self-acceptance is still in process for Adam. He knows that his life journey is to free himself from doubt and accept his life as it is. He discovered the techniques of shamanism, derived from ancient Native American traditions, through which he experienced ecstatic moments when he felt himself to be full of love and bliss. At first these only served to accentuate his internal conflict. He said to me, 'I want to be able to just be in my life, without conflict.' Once he had committed himself to using the tools of shamanism, he found himself slipping into an ease of being in his spiritual practice, which he had not expected and which delighted him.

Finally, he decided to marry his long-term partner.

What to Expect as the Remedy Works

Medorrhinum rebalances an energy body that has become wired up as a result of the hedonistic search for highs. The different aspects of your personality feel more integrated, so that you no longer oscillate between extremes of mood and behaviour. You normally have a tremendous passion and gusto for life, but if you are stuck in the pattern of this remedy you may feel that access to your soul is just out of reach. The remedy Medorrhinum stimulates your natural energy and channels your desire for exploration into accessing a deeper sense of soul. You may find that you can best develop your innate soul qualities by exploring simple practices like meditation.

Medorrhinum connects you with the essential core of yourself, so that you become less attracted to addictive experiences. It heals your addiction by prompting you to action. Through actualizing your plans and projects your life becomes more grounded. Medorrhinum helps unblock your creativity by freeing you of an exaggerated egotism. It expands your narcissistic search for pleasure into a concern for the well-being of others. You feel more love and compassion for others.

Soul Learning for Medorrhinum

You need to learn integrity, which involves integrating your desire for bliss with an ability to sink more into the real experiences already available to you.

Natrum Muriaticum

The key theme of the Natrum muriaticum energy pattern is trust. People get stuck in the Natrum muriaticum energy pattern when something has happened to them in the past which makes them wary. This could be the loss of someone important in their lives, or an incident of being badly let down. This is a remedy for major grief that does not heal. People who need it have difficulty coping with bereavement; they find it difficult to move on in life.

Natrum muriaticum is actually made from salt. In the Biblical story, Lot's wife was turned into a pillar of salt because she looked back. In terms of this remedy, this story suggests that if you are always looking back rather than moving forward in life, you risk becoming ossified in the energy pattern of homeopathically prepared salt.

One of the reasons Natrum muriaticum personalities find themselves unable to accept the loss of a loved one is that they feel they could have had so much more with that person than they actually had. The potential was not fulfilled. They may feel that their intimacy was somehow not intense enough. Perhaps they did not allow that person to get close or they did not fully connect with them. Perhaps they needed more love than the other person was willing or able to give, or perhaps they could not allow themselves to accept the love they were offered.

Grief and loss produce a protective armour around their hearts, which nonetheless fails to protect them. All it does is block the free flow of energy. It ends up preventing them from feeling any kind of love, so that they become more and more armoured against other people. People in the Natrum muriaticum pattern seem distant to other people, and they feel emotionally cut off themselves. They still have a soft centre which needs warmth and closeness, yet their defensive exterior can keep others away. This leads to a sense of abandonment and leaves them feeling bitter and resentful. These emotions only increase their sense of separation and ultimate aloneness.

People in the Natrum muriaticum pattern find it very difficult to forgive. Their experience of loss, abandonment or betrayal leaves them holding a lot of pain and resentment towards the person they feel is responsible. They blame the person they have lost for the emotional suffering they are going through. Their inability to forgive leads them to judge and blame others. When they stand in judgement over other people, they again feel separate from them. Their lack of forgiveness blocks the exchange of energy between themselves and others, so that they feel even more isolated.

Victor first came in to see me in 1985, complaining of being 'run down'. After a long discussion, it emerged that the real problem was that he was suffering from loneliness. His own particular way of dealing with emotions prevented him from relating easily to people. When he wasn't working, he needed time alone to un-wind, but once he'd recovered he found it difficult to drop his mood of isolation and let people in.

He took offence easily and got irritable. For instance, he felt that as a single man he had to make most of the effort to maintain friendships with others who were in families, and this annoyed him. When he was feeling piqued, he would not contact friends even though he wanted to see them and consequently suffered in his aloneness. He was rarely able to see matters from other people's point of view.

He worked in a hierarchical, bureaucratic organization and kept getting passed over for promotion. He felt very angry when younger people who were promoted above him told him what to do. He felt unappreciated by his bosses, which made him indignant, but he was unable to express this feeling constructively. In spite of feeling angry at being unrecognized, he realized that he was also afraid of responsibility. On a deeper level, he felt that he did not deserve recognition, but at the same time he was offended when it was not forthcoming. In spite of his own ambivalence, he described his position as unjust.

Victor felt shy and inadequate, and said he had been dogged all his life by the fact that his mother had rejected him. He had been very clingy as a baby, and apparently he did not do anything independently until he was two years old. His mother had become disoriented as a result of some psychiatric problems, so his father spent more time caring for him. The mother left home when he was five, for reasons that were not explained to him, and he did not meet her again until he was 38. Unfortunately this was not a positive or healing experience.

Victor complained that he had felt abandoned and worthless ever since he was a child. He experienced complex feelings towards women. He was emotionally distant towards them, and at times hostile. He said that he was unable to relate comfortably to women, but resented not getting their attention. He found feelings of sexual attraction difficult to handle, as his desire also brought up a primal fear of getting hurt. He described himself as very needy and demanding when in a sexual relationship. He had become extremely depressed in the past after a relationship had broken up, and since then had spent years without one.

When depressed, he felt inhibited and tried to hide himself, but he also felt exposed and raw, as if other people could see right inside him. He had become very isolated, depressed and at times suicidal, but he was afraid to confess his suicidal feelings because he worried that other people would be scared by them.

The remedy Natrum muriaticum gave Victor more confidence and, when he became more confident, his social skills improved. As he felt more comfortable socially, he got a better response from others. He gradually learned that he could choose to let go of the old familiar resentments he had built up to create a wall behind which he could not be reached. The grudges he held against people and his sense of indignation had become for him a source of false pride. In pride, he acted in a prickly, superior way. Other people then left him alone, which was excruciating for him. Until he took the remedy, he did not know how to break this painful pattern. Being conscious of it was not enough to make him change such a deep habit. He needed the energetic impetus of the remedy to help him shift out of that stuck perspective.

After being treated with Natrum muriaticum, Victor felt less suspicious of others' behaviour and motives. He was less tense, as he no longer had the need to defend himself and restrain his feelings all the time. He still got angry and indignant, but by expressing his emotions more fully he got rid of bad moods straightaway instead of allowing them to slowly simmer, colouring days at a time with negativity. Victor's deep depression took a couple of years (and several doses of the remedy) to go away.

As he was feeling more confident, Victor took the uncharacteristic risk of contacting an old girlfriend. She was someone he had previously been annoyed with over her not keeping to an arrangement, and they had had some rather abrasive interactions. But he had softened as a result of his homeopathic treatment, and when he saw her he was able to acknowledge their friendship and his feelings of attraction, which she responded to. They then moved out of London and bought a house together, and he allowed himself to settle into a very established relationship with her, which was consolidated by their marriage.

Although Victor explored several possibilities of leaving work and starting something new, nothing attracted him strongly enough to encourage him to let go of his job security. But now that he felt emotionally secure, he allowed himself to feel lighter, letting the child in him come out to play. Eventually he took early retirement and only worked part-time on a freelance basis. This gave him more time to pursue his own spiritual development through yoga and meditation.

What to Expect as the Remedy Works

If the remedy is indicated for you, Natrum muriaticum makes you feel safe enough to let go of the negative emotions that have imprisoned you inside your own mind. By rejecting introspective and secretive tendencies, you can open up to and trust others again. In dropping the need to keep scores, you no longer judge others in ways that are critical or condemning. In order to forgive, allow yourself to experience the emotional softness of compassion, rather than the hardness of judgement. Compassion converts the feeling of anger into one of mercy when you allow your heart to open towards others.

This remedy supports you in finding a way through the unfinished business of the past by helping you understand your own psychological pain and its relation to past experiences. Once you acknowledge this pain you can progress from a self-centred perspective to a more forgiving one. The most important thing the remedy will help you do is to learn to forgive. Then you can abandon your reserve and open up your heart to love again.

Natrum muriaticum allows you to go more deeply into your feelings. You experience your loss, rather than constantly brooding on and analysing old emotions. The remedy stimulates you to live more fully in each and every moment, rather than hanging on to the past or armouring yourself against the present.

Before taking the remedy your heart will have felt heavy and sad and you may have been unable to open yourself to relationships as a result of past griefs, disappointments and betrayals. Natrum muriaticum heals the deep grief and pain. It also heals old emotional wounds and opens you up to the experience of love and life. The remedy frees your energy to flow again, opening up your heart. You let go of stuck emotions and respond more appropriately to the current situation. You will find that you are living more in the present, and that you are able to experience the small gifts of love present in everyday interactions. You will also come to appreciate the deeper feelings of love and compassion which are part of your existential reality, if you can only tune in to that.

Soul Learning for Natrum Muriaticum

Try to trust in the greater wisdom of the universe, for you cannot always understand why you are forced to let go of people and situations you love, and move on. Find the courage to let go, and experience the pleasures of making new connections and of building new relationships. Try to open up to the experience of connectedness with others.

Nux Vomica

The key theme of the Nux vomica remedy pattern is a stressed response to challenges. People stuck in the energy pattern corresponding to Nux vomica feel overstretched and anxious about their ability to achieve their goals. They are hard-working and initially thrive on pressure, but after a time they become overstressed. They can respond to the challenge of living at such a pitch with irritability and anger. They live off their nerves, in a state of adrenaline which creates heightened sensitivity to noise and external stimulation. Noise can irritate them intensely. Their state of adrenaline often causes sleep problems: they wake in the early hours of the morning feeling wide awake and making lists of things to be done, sometimes giving up on sleep in order to pack more into the day. Otherwise they can lie awake for hours feeling overloaded, anxious and churning over their problems. In this state, their nervous tension reduces their ability to cope.

Such people are 'type A' personalities: intense, driven and goal-oriented. They are usually very good at what they do, but are often perfectionist and find it difficult to delegate. Other people may not be able to meet their high expectations, and they can be intolerant of those they consider less capable. They identify themselves very much with their work and are ambitious and competitive.

People stuck in the energy pattern of this remedy usually have problems with anger. They may not always express their anger, holding it inside and describing themselves as seething under the surface. Their rage can erupt like a volcano at any slight provocation, a sign that they have been suppressing resentful feelings for some time.

When things build up inside, they can no longer cope. They may have violent outbursts, shout, kick and break things. A tremendous frustration erupts, and they may feel driven to vent it in order to relieve their emotional state of tension.

Tony, aged 50, came in complaining of a state of energy collapse. He needed to drink lots of coffee in the morning to get going. The problem with using coffee or other stimulants in this way is that they can mask chronic exhaustion. The buzz produced by coffee does not come from real energy, but from a caffeine-induced adrenaline state.

He had been diagnosed with viral labyrinthitis, which affects the balance mechanism inside the ear and had left him weaving his way down the road. 'I've never felt so ill in my life.' Four years previously he had also developed testicular cancer, and one testicle had been removed. He had been tremendously anxious about it at the time, but was not aware of worrying about a recurrence at the time he consulted me.

In general Tony was very stressed and wound up. He habitually worked up to 12 hours a day running his own company. A perfectionist, he was unable to delegate. High levels of energy enabled him to drive himself hard, but his body was complaining. He held a tremendous level of tension in his body. His shoulders seized up regularly, and he also suffered from headaches and dizzy spells. He saw black spots in his visual field every time he turned his head, and had started to experience deafness in one ear, which was apparently caused by irritation of a nerve.

Tony kept his physical tension under control by playing lots of squash in a frenetic, combative manner. He was usually competitive: everything he did had to be done with as much gusto as possible. 'I put my all into everything I do.' The down side of living at this pitch of intensity was that he was frightened of his bottled-up energy. He felt that he might hurt other people, and that made him try to bottle it up even more. 'I can be seething inside, and then eventually I just explode and get really angry.'

Tony had a fast metabolism, which kept him slim and warm, with easy perspiration. He described himself as quick-tempered; he was selfish, intolerant and at times aggressive. He was unable to accept others' points of view. 'I don't suffer fools gladly.' But he was also hard on himself. He definitely needed approval and described himself as bashful and unable to accept praise, because he had grown up unaccustomed to receiving any.

Once he had taken the remedy Nux Vomica, Tony immediately relaxed and his pace slowed down, which did not seem to irritate him. He gave up drinking coffee and went back to playing tennis twice a week. He complained of a lack of the old adrenaline state on the tennis courts. He was no longer waking at 6 a.m. with a racing brain. He noticed that his energy was much better in phases, coming and going over the course of a day.

He still felt he had a slight temperature, with loose bowels, and was plagued by muscle tension. The physical symptoms became more intense for a few days after I gave him the remedy: he felt extremely hot and more exhausted. But within a week of taking the Nux vomica Tony's energy was very good and he was sleeping a lot better. He said that he no longer felt crippled by anxieties over cash flow problems in the business. He had used to feel stress in his stomach, producing the indigestion symptoms of dyspepsia. After the remedy he experienced far fewer griping pains in his stomach, and his bowel movements became firmer.

Tony's control issues were definitely improving, and he was more able to delegate. For the first time in years he decided to take time off work for a holiday. The excruciating tension in his body eased up at the same time that he stopped pushing himself beyond the limits of his endurance, both physically and psychologically.

What to Expect as the Remedy Works

After taking the remedy Nux Vomica there is usually a tremendous improvement in energy levels. Stress-related symptoms clear up rapidly. As tension is released you are more able to relax. You feel less tense and hurried. You are more able to be effective without having to drive yourself. As the pace of life slows down, you can once again appreciate the beauty of simple pleasures. You no longer feel like a coiled-up spring. Your irritability disappears along with your nervous tension.

Pent-up anger and irritability evaporate, leaving you more able to interact with others in a calmer and more engaged manner. You realize that you are not the only one good enough to do what needs to be done. Other people have their own capabilities and gifts and you realize you can make space to allow them to contribute a different perspective. Despite ceding control, you retain a sense of resolve in your own purpose, but you no longer miss out on life's pleasures because you are no longer too narrowly focused on achieving the goal that you have set yourself.

Soul Learning for Nux vomica

The journey is more important than reaching the goal, and life is more than a series of goals.

Phosphorus

People stuck in the energy pattern of Phosphorus often have problems with boundaries. While people with other remedy patterns need to let go of their sense of self, those in the Phosphorus energy pattern may need to define themselves more clearly. The boundaries between self and other people are particularly permeable for people who resonate with the Phosphorus pattern. A sociable temperament coupled with a sympathetic concern for others and an expansive tendency means that their own energy can diffuse outwards.

The positive side of this tendency can be seen in their abundant qualities of sympathy and empathy. Playful and good-humoured, they touch others a lot and enjoy maintaining eye contact. They care about others and can literally feel how other people's experiences affect them. They are often prepared to extend themselves for others, doing everything possible to provide help and support. Because they know exactly what is needed, the aid they offer is perfectly apt. On the negative side, they can't separate themselves adequately and they risk getting swamped by others' feelings. For example, they may feel someone else's depression so keenly that they become depressed themselves. They can even develop a headache when they are with someone suffering from migraine.

I recognize this blurring of identity from my own experience, when personal boundaries have seemed too flimsy to protect a precarious sense of self. I was struck by what I experienced as a kind of energetic contamination when I was with a friend's husband in the hyper phase of manic depression. I felt my own thinking become as agitated as I presumed his mental processes were. I experienced the same nervousness, restlessness and longing to escape which he appeared to be going through in his chaotic internal state. I was amazed when his wife said that she was able to meditate in his presence, even though he was constantly moving, talking excitedly, exclaiming and moaning. As a result of her comment, I had the idea of using meditation techniques to re-stabilize myself after getting back home. If in a Phosphorus state, it is helpful to meditate on the image of your body being rooted to the earth, as a means of grounding yourself.

People needing this remedy are impressionable, picking up on subtle cues and changes in atmospheres. They can be disturbed by any imbalance in their environment, whether its the change of electrical ions that accompanies a thunderstorm, bad 'feng shui', or a change in their friend's mood. They can also be destabilized by surprises and exciting events. It is difficult for them to know their own mind, they are so easily influenced by companions. They find themselves seduced by others' opinions or moods and tend to bend and sway with the wind.

They can lose their centre, becoming swayed by different thoughts, feelings and impressions. They feel unstable and risk losing sight of what they are doing in their own life, becoming distracted by new ideas, interesting projects or the latest spiritual teacher. They can be spiritually evolved and often have psychic or clairvoyant abilities, such as the ability to anticipate events or read the energy fields of others. But when unstable they feel overwhelmed by their awareness of psychic phenomena and become fearful. They feel unsafe and afraid of unknown spiritual forces or entities, as well as the dark, death and illness. When their boundaries collapse they hate to be left alone because they are afraid of some impending misfortune, and they need a lot of reassurance from friends and family.

Linda had been married for over a decade, but she had fallen in love with someone in her spiritual group. Her husband had become depressed over personal problems in his own life and he was no longer able to connect with her properly. Although her job in journalism was glamorous and exciting, she often felt empty instead of stimulated or fulfilled.

Over a four-month period, we worked on resolving her feelings of conflict about the two men in her life. Linda felt pulled between her familiar, settled relationship, in which she could go on to have children, and the excitement of a new relationship in which she could share spiritual experiences and explorations. The situation made her feel very vulnerable, because she did not really know what she wanted. She was filled with longing for her lover, but at the same time she behaved in a clingy way with her husband. She needed support and reassurance, and she did not really trust in her attraction toward her lover. A huge fear of making mistakes paralysed her. Linda felt this stemmed from the regret she felt about not healing her relationship with her father before he died. She had not been able to tell him that she loved him because of the way she felt alienated by all the problems around his alcoholism.

Her symptoms manifested themselves in physical symptoms such as an irritated vagina. Linda did not want to have intercourse, and a cervical smear showed changes due to one of the large family of wart viruses.

After her first dose of Phosphorus, Linda's next cervical smear proved clear. She experienced a surge of grounded energy and a sense of overall well-being. She felt much more open emotionally. Her levels of desire increased and she was able to make love again in comfort with her husband.

Next the remedy produced a more intense desire for her own space. She wanted to spend all her time in her meditation room. She was more aware of her own need for safety and for finding a safe place to be herself in. The remedy was helpful in clarifying the central issues in her emotional situation, so that she no longer felt that she was in an undifferentiated morass of ambiguous feelings.

After a second dose of her constitutional remedy Linda had a lot more dreams, which she felt were significant. One was about a relationship between lovers that required a leap of faith to go forward, but she did not interpret the message of the dream as a simple invitation to pursue the relationship with her lover. 'Instead I felt a big "no" welling up, and it helped me start letting go of him and focusing on my own faith – through my mediation practice.' This realization was followed by a dream in which she said goodbye to her lover, turned to her husband and then climbed up a mountain with him.

Linda began to accept what she had seen as loneliness in pursuing her spiritual path, and was more tolerant of her partner's lack of interest in her spiritual quest.

remedies for the soul

She was less fearful of the changes that would come with having a child. Because she was feeling more open and their sexual relationship had improved, they stopped using contraceptives. Her dreams became very sexual and put her in touch with her sexual power. Initially she found this scary, until she decided to use this energy to enrich her sexual experience.

What to Expect as the Remedy Works

This remedy usually has an immediate effect. You feel so full of energy that you're bubbling with it. It seems like a heady state, but taking Phosphorus creates more clarity about which feelings are really yours and which belong to other people. Before taking the remedy, you were likely to have been so empathetic and responsive to other peoples' internal states that you would do just about anything to relieve their pain. With the greater clarity which Phosphorus brings, it becomes easier for you to work out appropriate ways to respond to someone else's existential anguish.

If you are in the Phosphorus energy pattern, then you are someone who is on the path of service (see page 58). The remedy will help you clarify the ways you can best be of help.

You also may need to create ways of making yourself feel safe. Taking the remedy helps you learn to be more selfish, in the sense of recognizing that you have your own needs. Phosphorus gives you the resources to meet these needs.

Soul Learning for Phosphorus

You need to become more grounded and centred in the core of your being. You need to stabilize your changeable emotional nature by grounding yourself in a sense of history and continuity between past and present, self and other.

Pulsatilla

The central theme in the Pulsatilla remedy pattern is emotional neediness. The person stuck in this energy pattern feels quite empty inside and hates to be alone, which is when they sink into this state of emptiness. They need to have company around and will do just about anything to please others. They are very compliant and tend to go along with the plans or wishes of others, just so long as they are included. They may not know what they themselves want to do, because they're so used to putting others first.

They are usually soft, sweet and accommodating, and other people like to spend time with them. They are emotionally open and sensitive. They have sympathetic personalities and are good listeners, responding to others' emotional needs. But they also need to talk about themselves and expect plenty of support and sympathy from others.

Early emotional wounding may have occurred somewhere in their history, which has left them feeling abandoned. This could be due to early separation from their mother, or due to their parents' divorce or death. Experiences like these leave them feeling bereft, lonely and needing a tremendous amount of support. If they cannot get the support they need, they will become needy and demanding in friendships and intimate relationships, in ways that are perceived as clingy. Children often show their needs by becoming clingy, wanting to be held all the time and crying whenever they are put down. Sometimes this behaviour succeeds in getting their needs met: their carer feels sorry for them and showers them with attention, affection and cuddles. At other times this behaviour is very irritating and results in the child being pushed away.

This kind of behaviour may be repeated in adulthood with the same results. Some of the people locked in this pattern manage to attract people to care for them throughout their lives. They form co-dependent relationships in which their partners feel good about supplying all the support they need. Others find that they are continually being pushed away as a result of making their partners feel smothered. This exacerbates the abandoned feeling which people requiring Pulsatilla are struggling with.

The loss of loved ones or the break-up of a relationship are particularly painful for people in this energy pattern. Such misfortunes result in a tearful depression, where they feel they just cannot cope any more. They may go into a flat, depressive, unresponsive state, as if their life-force has drained out of them, punctuated by outbursts of crying. Crying actually relieves the depression and acts as a positive venting of their grief. The grief needs to be accepted and allowed, and it will probably go on for some time, at least for as long as it is necessary. Depression is something Pulsatilla types are particularly prone to, feeling weepy, empty and without purpose in their lives if their personal relationships are not close and nurturing. The depression tends to lift when they are in the company of warm people, unlike much deeper depressive states, such as those associated with the Aurum energy pattern (see page 180).

Close relationships are of paramount importance to such people, and they tend to define themselves through their primary relationships. They may long for a close and loving relationship, and when they have found a mate they require a high level of intimacy to feel whole. They feel bereft whenever their partner behaves in a distant manner towards them, and find it difficult to be self-sufficient.

Bonnie had a difficult relationship with Michael, the father of her child: he took refuge from intimacy in his workaholism and found it difficult to open up to her and share his life. For some years they had been locked in a dance of distance, where as one moved closer the other retreated. This repetitive cycle of neediness, rejection and abandonment was wounding both of them deeply. Nevertheless, Bonnie believed in the bond of love between them, which kept her 'hanging on in there', hoping to work through the fears of intimacy in their relationship and eventually break into the more nurturing feelings they still had for each other.

Bonnie had to work on containing her own destructive and attacking impulses, which were based on a belief that men were not much good to her. Her father had been unloving and dominating, and she felt he had taken out his frustrations about his loveless marriage on her. Since then she had protected herself from disappointment by putting on a cynical and belittling attitude towards men.

During our work together, Bonnie acknowledged that her very first relationship had been with a man who was very loving and nurturing of her, and she realized that even by the age of 18 she was uncomfortable with feelings of intimacy because her relationship with her father was so damaged. Bonnie said that she had not been able to tolerate experiencing all these good feelings. They just made her feel increasingly anxious, and eventually she drove him away.

I chose the remedy Pulsatilla for her because its energy pattern resonated with the very painful state of abandonment she experienced whenever her beloved pushed her away. After taking it she experienced tremendous warmth towards herself and others, and a sometimes euphoric joy. It was out of this experience that she was able to heal the hurt in herself and to begin to look at and accept her own part in relationship difficulties.

Bonnie owned up to her fear of intimacy, which underlay her, at times, desperate loneliness and sense of abandonment. She began to honour the flame of love she kept for Michael, working hard at acknowledging the softness she felt towards him rather than retreating into her habitual harsh and judgemental position. She felt at times it was more painful to remain soft in the face of his ambivalence and to keep expressing her love for him, but she decided to stay true to her own deeper truth. While her friends advised her to end the relationship, she knew that the deep love that existed between them was of fundamental importance to her. She realized that in spite of their difficulties, he was her true love, and that the relationship was providing a crucible for emotional transformation through which she could heal her own wounds.

Now that she had experienced love as something existing within herself, Bonnie felt less needy of her partner and more able to accept the love he could show her. As she became less demanding, he became more giving, and they began to define better ways for their relationship to work as a family, in spite of the fact that they chose not to live together. Bonnie realized that their relationship was about a deep soul connection, and in spite of the conflicts they experienced on a personality level, she continued to honour the deep love underneath their power struggles.

What to Expect as the Remedy Works

By releasing the energy locked into an experience of emotional deprivation, Pulsatilla stimulates your whole being. You begin to fill in the gaping emptiness inside that drives you to reach out for human contact so desperately. This remedy heals your emotional wounding and sense of abandonment. It will allow you to find the internal resources to meet your own needs rather than trying to rely on others to fulfil them. It will dissolve the sense of isolation you feel, enabling you to receive whatever is actually available. You no longer feel bereft, weepy and in need of sympathy. You no longer attempt to manipulate the emotions of others through cajoling, demands, threats or tantrums. You are able to look at your own emotional needs and start to find ways to explore them yourself. In the end you will release your tremendous need, which paradoxically can allow you to experience more love. Instead of feeling that whatever you get is never enough, you are able to luxuriate in the affection and attention of others.

The path to healing involves learning to be alone, discovering who you are inside and developing the ability to draw on internal resources. Through understanding and healing the pain attached to old experiences you can learn to love yourself. You can enjoy your propensity to give, and be appreciative of all the things friends and family contribute to your happiness.

Soul Lesson for Pulsatilla

You need to find love within yourself, rather than expecting others to meet your emotional needs.

Sepia

The central theme in the Sepia energy pattern is that of feeling careworn and overburdened. People with this energy pattern are ceaselessly busy looking after others, so that there is little or no time for looking after themselves. Over a period of time they become worn out as a result of giving and caring for others. This can lead to a lack of care for themselves and then to a lack of care for others. They feel unable to take any more. They eventually end up with a feeling of emotional flatness and indifference, especially towards the loved ones who may come to be seen as the cause of all the stress. They describe it as reaching the stage where they feel that they haven't enough emotional resources for themselves, let alone any to spare for someone else.

People stuck in the Sepia pattern may neglect to do any of the things that would feed their spirit or nurture their emotions, and the result is that they lose motivation, as well as their lust for life. The apathetic state which they retreat into is only occasionally relieved when they do something that produces lots of endorphins (positive brain chemicals), like exercise or dancing. If they can get over their feelings of antipathy towards sex, love-making also helps them feel better and more in touch with themselves. But this positive feeling lasts only as long as the chemical state produced by the feel-good endorphins. When not leading an active life or exercising, they feel tired and miserable. They tend to concentrate on what they have not got rather than on everything they do have.

For such people, most things are experienced as demands. For instance, they find the input needed to sustain a close relationship with their partner too demanding, and they experience their partner's desire for them to spend time together as a demand rather than a joy or a support. Cooking a nice meal is too much of an effort and socializing is too tiring.

This energy pattern often develops in parents of young children, because of the lack of support in our society for this exhausting period of life. They become gradually depleted by years of broken nights and long hours in the service of children and perhaps spouses. Their loving feelings are eventually masked by fatigue, so that they are only dimly aware that the only emotional responses they now have towards their families are ones of irritation at their relentless demands. At other times they may become anxious that they have lost the ability to have fun times and loving moments with their families.

To such people it feels as if they have no more energy available to deal with the needs of their partner. For both men and women sexual energy tends to be low, because of the difficulty they find in connecting to other people from their drained emotional state. Sex in particular becomes just one more trial, instead of something to be enjoyed for the pleasure and feeling of closeness it brings.

The emotional state of people in the Sepia pattern is one of disconnectedness, even when the partner is there and, from the outside, it appears to be a happy family setup. Inside, however, it feels like a struggle to get through each day, and there is just no energy to summon up enthusiasm or joy.

Such a colourless and devitalized experience of life creates a mood of depression, which people in the Sepia state may be hardly aware of. Their emotions shut down, and they experience an emotional stillness inside which is not one of tranquillity. They find it difficult to laugh or cry, or even experience much joy or pain. It is as if there is not enough energy to animate the person any more: somehow it has all been used up. This state of depression is a numb feeling rather than one that is full of angst. Tears may roll down their cheeks, and yet they can find it difficult to say what it is they feel so depressed about. They ask themselves, 'Is this all there is to life?'

Sepia people experience a constant mood of irritability coupled with fatigue. When loved ones try to get some kind of response, they can lash out with venom. Usually it is an irritation that comes up over household tasks and the endless daily round of domestic jobs that need to be done. Because they have a penetrating mind and tend to be frank to the point of bluntness, they can make astute observations which go right to the point. They are shrewd judges of character and know just where to aim, using their sharp tongue as a means of keeping people away.

Since the Sepia energy pattern also upsets hormonal balance, all these feelings can become more acute for women around the time of menstruation, after giving birth, or at menopause.

Carol, a woman in her early thirties, came to see me for treatment for polycystic ovaries. She had been on the contraceptive pill for years and when she decided to try for a baby, she found her fertility was reduced because of the condition. She had typical signs of the syndrome: acne, weight gain and excess hair.

Her sex drive had been high in the past, but it had definitely reduced, and for a while she thought that was the reason why she was not conceiving. She had a good relationship with her husband: they had been together for 12 years and had an easy and companionable relationship at the weekends. During the week they were both busy working and keeping up with their friends independently. She had begun to worry about their habitual self-sufficiency, because she knew they would have to pull together when they became parents.

Carol had not shared these fears with her partner, nor that on a deeper level she was ambivalent about her ability to be a good mother. Her relationship with her own mother had long been fraught, so she found it difficult to connect with her maternal side. She was not very close to her sister's children and felt guilty about not spending much time with them. She tended to over-compensate by buying them lots of presents.

After she took Sepia, Carol realized that she needed to share her feelings with her partner. This improved their emotional intimacy, but he said he definitely did not want to get obsessional about the whole topic of fertility. As far as he was concerned, he was happy to have a child, but if it did not happen he would prefer to accept that rather than go down the route of medically-assisted fertility.

Carol realized that in order to nurture their relationship she would have to give up some of the things she liked doing, like going to the gym a few times a week and seeing her friends on her own. Yet it was also important for her to nurture herself. She was someone who always had to be doing something, and under the action of her remedy she began to explore more contemplative activities, like taking long walks in the park.

She found that by letting go of the expectation on herself that she should entertain her sister's kids, she could sit back and appreciate them. She found their immediacy and engagement with the world refreshing and enjoyed their comments. Because she had not had the experience of receiving from her own mother, she needed to learn how to take in love. She shared these thoughts with her sister, and this helped their relationship, which had become distant because her sister felt Carol did not accept her children.

The Sepia cleared up her skin, presumably because it was working on her ovarian condition. Her periods became more regular, and the hormonal imbalance improved enough for her to conceive, which she did within a few months. Sepia balances the oestrogen and progesterone levels in the body, clearing up a lot of gynaecological problems. It helps women to resolve the conflicts they experience around the social polarities of masculine and feminine, dependence and independence, and mothering versus career. It is not the only remedy capable of doing this; as always in homeopathy, any one of a range of remedies can do this, depending on the particular energy pattern you find yourself in.

What to Expect as the Remedy Works

When Sepia releases your blocked energy, you will recall what it feels like to be alive. You feel engaged in what you're doing again, and you feel your feelings with your old intensity. Your stilled emotions flex and wake up. This might mean that the path back to wellness may not always be smooth, especially for those around you. But for someone like you, who has been feeling so numb, any eruption of emotions will contribute to your feeling more alive again.

The remedy recharges your depleted body and raises energy levels. It stimulates your endocrine glands, rebalancing hormone levels and ensuring that your body functions at an optimum level. If this is the correct remedy for you, it will enable you to take in more resources from your environment; physically, emotionally and spiritually. You will make the time to look after your needs on each of these levels. Sepia motivates you to take pleasure for yourself and make your own needs a priority as a requisite for caring for others.

Sepia helps you reconnect with your loving and loyal disposition in close relationships, while also helping you discover that you too need means of expressing yourself, whether it is through work or some creative pursuit. You need your own space; without it you risk closing down emotionally. The remedy helps you to realize that you cannot always make things all right for other people. Often what is important is just to be there when someone is in need, rather than doing things which you think will help.

For giving not to become draining, it needs to come from the right orientation. In order that you do not suffer from burnout, your giving needs to spring from compassion rather than pity. Pity is where you feel sorry for someone else's suffering; compassion is where you feel for their suffering and you are able to act towards them with loving kindness.

Soul Learning for Sepia

You need to learn to receive love. When you give love to others through acts of service, try to experience it as coming from this source of love outside yourself, rather than from your own personal reserves.

Silica

The central theme of the Silica pattern is sensitivity. It is a theme that has double-sided consequences, for it is both a blessing and sometimes a burden to be sensitive in the world in which we live. There is a tremendous emotional delicacy in this energy pattern, which means that the person is vulnerable to the way they are treated: if treated with insensitivity by others, they do not develop a protective thick skin but instead find ways to protect their inner world from possible brutalization. Usually loyal and restrained, under pressure they retreat emotionally, trusting enough to open up only with difficulty. In their own home environment, among friends, they relax and become entertaining, witty and even obstinately opinionated.

As family therapist Steve Biddulph says, children are not born shy. Shyness is a response to an experience of the world as an unsafe place. If Silica children are treated insensitively, they will retreat into their own inner world. The Silica energy pattern is thus one which people can develop as a result of early experiences.

Shyness is a great handicap, for it prevents people affected by it from connecting with others. It stops them reaching out to the world and tasting the range of experiences available. If they do reach out and have a less than inviting response, they close up again and retreat into their shells. This tends to narrow down the possibilities open to them because they respond to their own insecurity by holding on too tightly to a need for structure.

Because of their sensitivity, they have a feeling of vulnerability and a fear of getting hurt which can lead them to avoid taking the risk of getting close to other people. This cautiousness makes them uncomfortable socially. In spite of being capable as well as intelligent and emotionally perceptive, Silica personalities feel shy, awkward and easily embarrassed. It takes time for them to open up. They feel much safer with one-to-one communication. The difficulties they have around socializing lead to a lack of confidence, even though they are often talented in many other areas, such as in literary or artistic pursuits.

Other people can interpret their shyness as standoffishness or superiority, especially because the shyness is in an intelligent person who can be very articulate when they want to be. This often results in the shy person being left alone even more. What they really need are more invitations from more confident people, allowing them the opportunity of experiencing interactions that will show them that the ground does not open up underfoot and swallow them if they make a social gaffe.

Shy people are very much concerned with how they come across to others. The anxiety they experience about any kind of public appearance can be seen as a kind of inverse egotism, in which the person stuck in this energy pattern is overly aware of and sensitized to their image. Underlying the concern with how they come across to others is a sense of inadequacy. Some people with the Silica pattern learn effective ways of coping with and masking this inadequacy; they succeed in developing ways of being in the world which enable them to project a self-confident air. However, they risk hardening so much emotionally in order to deal with the world that they can have problems with receiving.

The inner world of people with the Silica pattern is very rich and a source of creativity. But it is also a lonely place. Silica people may find themselves alone in their own fantasy world, or they may connect with the spirit world. One young man I treated, whose father had been violent towards him and whose mother had been largely absent, took to conversing with spirit figures in treetops as he walked the streets.

For such people, the spirit world can become more real than the ordinary, quotidian world. The Silica energy pattern of sensitivity sharpens people's innate psychic faculties and creates connections with the world of spirit. They can be receptive to energy fields in a number of ways. For example they may be able to sense when people are about to telephone, or if someone is going through some difficulties. They can have premonitory dreams or feelings, or intuitive perceptions that enable them to read cards or hands. They may be able to perform telekinesis. They may also be afraid of their psychic abilities because this can connect them to others in ways they find uncomfortable.

On a physical level, they can have problems with the spine, such as scoliosis, which is connected with the theme of rigidity in this remedy. They may also have difficulty taking nutrition from their food, because of malabsorption syndromes. This is connected with the theme of finding it difficult to receive nourishment in life. The remedy Silica promotes the healthy healing of physical as well as emotional scars.

Elizabeth, a 10-year-old girl, was brought to see me because of problems sleeping. It took one or two hours for her to get to sleep, and she often got up again. She was very slow and dreamy in the evenings, taking ages to wash and brush her teeth. She pottered around looking at things, getting distracted and forgetting what she was supposed to be doing. Elizabeth was also very slow eating her dinner.

When she tried to sleep, however, the problem seemed to be that she was too alert and could not switch off her busy mind. She had a very active imagination and seemed to be absorbed in her own world. At other times she seemed to worry too much about what was happening with her friendships, or about someone else's problems. She would worry about trivial things, like what she was going to take into school the next day.

She was sensitive to pathos and seemed frightened by clowns and scary stories. She still needed a nightlight on quite often when she slept. She had always liked her mother sleeping with her, and definitely slept much better when they shared a bed. She could not sleep if she tried to stay over at other girls' homes. But in other ways she was quite self-reliant, and could occupy herself creating things, drawing, dancing or making music. She was serious and well-behaved, but vulnerable to feeling left out or teased. She hated to be thought of as a 'freak' in any way. She complained of feeling lonely.

She suffered a great many colds and bouts of flu and tonsillitis, and her glands seemed chronically swollen. She was often weak and tired, and did not seem to have much physical stamina. She got sweaty when she was anxious, and worried a lot about every test and exam, although she was very bright and always did well at school.

Silica cleared up Elizabeth's tendency to infections and improved her energy dramatically. She no longer needed to flop down on the sofa as soon as she got in from school. Her swollen glands returned to a normal size once she stopped picking up repeated sore throats.

The remedy improved her confidence and reduced her anxiety levels, so she was able to switch off and get to sleep more easily. She took occasional doses of the remedy over the next few years, and it always cleared up her infections and boosted her energy and stamina.

When her periods started, Elizabeth became unbalanced again and developed spots on her face, which made her feel shy in social settings. Her periods were quite painful, and she felt weak and nauseated for the first day or two of her bleed.

She still felt a bit isolated because of her sensitive nature, and preferred close friendships where she could talk intimately rather than hanging around with a group of girls. She was very aware of the environment around her, and picked up on atmospheres. She was cautious and would observe for some time until she knew what was going on before feeling courageous enough to participate. She worried about others and would stick up for other girls at school, even though she found it difficult to speak up for herself. She was sensitive to rudeness and injustice.

The remedy helped her periods settle into a regular pattern and cleared up the pain. Her acne became worse for the first few weeks – although the rate of healing was much better – and then improved. This boosted her self-esteem so that she felt happier with herself.

Elizabeth, now 16, began a long relationship with a boy with whom she was very close for some years. By the time she went to college to pursue an art degree, she was aware that they were moving apart but she was anxious about breaking up because she did not want to hurt him, and also because of her own fear of loneliness. Again, Silica gave her the confidence to separate and then to adapt to demanding university life.

What to Expect as the Remedy Works

Silica stimulates your energy. It clears up any infections that are depleting you physically. Your susceptibility to infections improves and the background feeling of being unwell disappears. Your immune system functions more efficiently and your rate of healing and recovery improves. Your energy becomes reliable and you have the stamina to take exercise or to complete projects. Getting involved in what you are doing in your life makes you less concerned with how others perceive you.

If this is the appropriate remedy for you, taking Silica will soften the hardness you have built up in response to the harshness of the outside world. It refines your personal awareness so that you no longer feel insulted by the insensitivities of others. You feel more confident about yourself and less intimidated in social settings. You value your own strengths, such as your quick mind, your perceptiveness and your emotional intelligence. You no longer hide behind your intellectual faculties and are more able to receive positive input from others.

Because you can trust in yourself, you can trust others more easily. The remedy also opens up your psychic awareness so that you feel more in touch with the spiritual realm. You feel more comfortable with this, and are no longer afraid that your clairvoyance might somehow leave you exposed to harmful influences. The soul channels this level of sensitivity into your spiritual growth.

Soul Learning for Silica

You need to connect with a wider source of energy so that you can take in more energy and charge yourself up.

Staphysagria

The key issue in the Staphysagria remedy pattern is frustration, which is internalized because there is no outlet for these feelings. The Staphysagria energy pattern develops when people are in a situation they cannot change. Intense feelings of rage build up, but because they feel powerless they cannot express their anger. They often feel indignant about being prevented from following their own calling.

This often happens in people whose dispositions are basically sweet: people who find it difficult to acknowledge their own power because they see anger as a negative emotion and something to feel ashamed of. They may constantly give their power away, allowing others to make decisions and choices for them, even to dominate or bully them. In work situations, they may be too afraid to confront their boss, either through lack of confidence or for fear of being sidelined or perhaps losing their job.

One woman constantly felt powerless because of her partner's lack of commitment to their relationship. She said that he always kept her waiting. She felt unable to ask him to make definite plans in case this made him withdraw even further, and he responded by never showing any form of commitment. She couldn't get on with her life because of the tremendous amount of time she spent fantasizing about the relationship and indulging in romantic daydreaming, and then dealing with her feelings of rejection and abandonment whenever he did not make contact. All this energy locked up in her fantasies about the relationship kept her from applying herself to more fulfilling activities. After taking Staphysagria, within a few months she broke away from this destructive situation, which had been going on for years.

The Staphysagria energy pattern is likely to form around romantic sexual relationships, where lack of confidence often leads people to think it is all their fault if things are not going well. They get stuck in situations where they are treated like doormats, because somewhere deep inside they feel they are worthless, and at times they behave like self-sacrificing martyrs. This is not like the soul definition of service, which is an act performed in the spirit of love, without strings attached. In a Staphysagria pattern, people have complex motives – a need for approval, guilt, duty – which drive them to do things for others that they then resent doing.

People in this remedy pattern have had their boundaries invaded. They may have internalized an abusive attitude so that they do not like themselves any more. As a result of experiences where others have not respected them, they have lost their own sense of self-respect.

People in this energy pattern often have dreams about their teeth falling out. The founder of psychoanalysis, Sigmund Freud, linked such dreams to problems with the libido. Libido, in his original sense, referred to the life-force. In the Staphysagria pattern the flow of the life-force is severely constricted. Because they feel unable to express what they really need to do, and because of the limitations of their situation, these people's energy gets misdirected inside, into resentment and frustration.

The obstruction in the free flow of energy can sometimes be channelled into an artistic poetic sensibility, producing some tremendously creative work. The spirit is indomitable and will try to find a way to express itself, however limited the circumstances are.

Maria, a middle-aged woman, came in suffering from multiple sclerosis, a disease where the sheaths of the spinal chords progressively degenerate, causing neurological symptoms. It had started in her twenties and, although the neurological episodes were infrequent and only mildly disabling, she was worried that they were getting worse. Before having children she had been busy and driven in her job as a legal secretary. She was indignant about the fact that she'd had to leave work after the birth of her second child, and that now all the domestic duties fell relentlessly on her shoulders.

She rarely went out in the evening because she was too tired after looking after her two children and her husband's mother, who lived with them. Since her mother-in-law had joined the family, Maria felt ignored and acutely resentful. The mother seemed to have her son wrapped around her little finger, and he would not listen to his wife's complaints. The elderly woman needed a lot of care, but Maria had noticed that she conveniently refused to do whatever she did not feel like doing. She was grumpy and apparently treated Maria like a piece of furniture.

The marriage was under a lot of strain, and Maria did not want to remain in it. Their sexual relationship was more or less over. Maria said she was staying only for the kids, and so she tried not to 'rock the boat'. She would lose her temper with the children over silly things, but she did not dare row with her husband because he easily got into a fit of rage. She said he had become more domineering, and she could not find a way of redressing the balance. Most of the time she was sweet and compliant, although, inside, she seethed with resentment. She was afraid of divorcing in case her multiple sclerosis got much worse, leaving her unfit for work. She could not believe she had become stuck in this situation. She also seemed to me to be depressed, although she did not complain of this directly.

When she consulted me, Maria was in the active phase of the disease, which caused numbness down one side of her torso. She was worried that her eyesight was beginning to be affected, which frightened her. Whenever she sat and brooded on her lot, she said that she was more aware of numbness in the affected parts of her body.

The next time I saw Maria, after she had taken Staphysagria, her mood was brighter and she was livelier. She told me that her eyesight had improved immediately, and that she hadn't had any further episodes of numbness.

remedies for the soul

The remedy had also put her in touch with her desires, and she had become more proactive about trying to get attention. The situation with her husband was just the same, but she had been having more fun with her children. She said she had not noticed how they had come to feel quite distant; she had been so wrapped up in her own problems that she had not taken the time for heart-to-hearts with them. Her older daughter had obviously realized that her parents were not very close and took her mother out shopping and to the movies. Once Maria started taking more of an interest in her children and making some time for them, her energy actually started to improve.

When her mother-in-law grumbled at her, she no longer smiled sweetly: she just left the room as soon as she had done what she had come in to do, and occasionally she erupted into uncharacteristic rudeness. Her husband responded to his mother's complaints by having a big tantrum, but Maria surprised them both by shouting back. The end result was that he ended up spending a bit more time caring for his mother himself, and came to see how demanding she could be.

Maria stayed in remission from the multiple sclerosis for a longer period of time, and found that taking the Staphysagria minimized any physical problems she had when it did recur. Over a period of time it became clear that the homeopathic treatment was stopping the condition from progressing. Consequently, Maria was able to focus on finding constructive ways to improve her domestic situation.

What to Expect as the Remedy Works

Taking Staphysagria dissolves your intense irritation and frustration. It allows you to use the emotional energy previously spent on containing strong emotions to reclaim a knowledge of your own power. Once you recognize your own strength, you regain your mental and emotional agility and access your creativity once again. You can express yourself with confidence and flair. You can stand up for what's important to you, saying 'no' to things you don't want and saying 'yes' to life-affirming opportunities.

As I have described, the Staphysagria energy patterns develop in someone when they are in a situation that cannot be changed. What Staphysagria does is help you find a more fluid and less self-destructive response to that situation. It changes your perception of your circumstances. Instead of seeing them as a trap, because the remedy frees up obstructed energy you experience a sense of freedom, despite the circumstantial limitations. The remedy allows you to reclaim your own power and to integrate it into your own personality structure so that you can be appropriately assertive. When we are feeling confident, there is often no need for anger, because others sense that we have good boundaries in place and that there is no point in attempting to push us around.

Soul Learning for Staphysagria

To feel free despite the limitations of your circumstances, you need to make appropriate boundaries between the claims of others and your own needs, so that you can make the space for your own creativity.

Stramonium

The central theme of the Stramonium remedy pattern is one of sheer terror, a feeling of being threatened in a fundamental way. The awareness of how fragile our claim on life is creates an existential void. Issues of safety become paramount for those who find themselves in this energy pattern, because they perceive the world not just as hostile, but as violent. This distorted energy pattern is created by situations of real or perceived danger and threat which forever change the person's sense of safety and solidity. These situations are usually ones which have occurred earlier in the person's life, but sometimes they are things which have happened to their parents. The Stramonium energy pattern is often the result of witnessing a violent incident. People stuck in this pattern become afraid of violence to a degree that can be almost phobic.

One young man had developed severe and frightening epilepsy during his childhood. His terrified energy pattern was traced by me to his mother's pregnancy with him, during which she had experienced a lot of violence in her relationship with his father, whom she subsequently left. I prescribed the remedy Stramonium because of this young man's mother's fear for her own survival while he was in the womb. The result was a tremendous improvement in the frequency and intensity of his epileptic seizures.

As a result of their existential fear, people in this energy pattern develop an intense emotional neediness. They feel utterly alone and abandoned, as if they are being left to face danger in a completely unsupported environment. They have a desperate need for protection and for safety. Fright becomes lodged inside them, typically leading to nightmares. They develop phobias. They are especially fearful of deep water, of putting their head under the water, and of the dark. The dark is scary because it represents the unconscious, the shadow, the unknown, the void or evil, depending on the person's particular belief system. Some religions define evil as a monstrous force for ill which is external to the person – this is exactly how the person in the Stramonium state feels about the hostile forces they encounter. They feel afraid of contamination or possession by dark forces. They are afraid of being overwhelmed.

They feel a great need for light and an intense need for the company of others. If they cannot have company they will want the comforting noise of the television or radio – anything so long as they can hear the sound of other human voices. They do not want to be alone and they feel very threatened if their relationship looks like it is falling apart. Because of their fear of abandonment, people in the Stramonium pattern will do anything to stay together with their partner.

Mona came to see me in an extremely tense and agitated state. She got particularly anxious in the evenings, suffering palpitations which prevented her from sleeping. She worried about the fact that she was not progressing in life, and also worried about how her children were managing.

Mona had started stammering at the age of three. Her father would beat her, and Mona was terrified of him as a child; she did not see him at all after leaving home. She suffered from asthma and frequent bronchitis, as well as eczema. Physically Mona was extremely tense; her back was painful and her whole left shoulder and neck were so stiff and tight that her head felt pulled round to the left. Her jaw cracked constantly and she would grind her teeth at night.

Mona felt she had never been able to get on with her life and was horrified to find herself still working as a hospital orderly after some years in the job. She tried to drink to relax at night, but the alcohol gave her restless dreams and broken sleep. As a result of all this anxiety, Mona became completely enervated. Being in this state left her exposed to voices which seemed to come from another world. When out walking, Mona would hear the voices of dead relatives telling her they were looking after her, giving reassurance and guidance. At first she was too scared of these voices to listen to their messages. When it did sink in that they were supportive, she was still anxious because she felt the messages of concern left an onus on her to make drastic changes. She didn't feel able to respond to this challenge.

For many years Mona had worked at menial jobs that were way beneath her abilities. She would not aim for something more fulfilling because of her fear of failure. She hid behind the constant stammering and used her phone phobia as an excuse for not changing jobs.

The remedy Stramonium immediately released the spasm in her neck and upper back. Mona's confidence improved. She changed jobs, although the new one proved to be demanding and left her no time for herself. She got used to having to make phone calls but still found it difficult to answer calls because of the uncertainty of not knowing who or what to expect.

Mona decided to do some speech therapy, and explored other occupations by taking courses that repeatedly revealed her many aptitudes and talents. She enrolled on an interior design course and discovered a talent for it. The teacher wanted her to work with him, but she was unable to take the financial risk of stopping full-time work. Her partner began training as an accountant while she kept the household going, and they moved into a bigger house. She spent hours decorating it and developed a passion for classical music – which seemed to be her form of meditation. Her anxieties loosened their hold and she was able to stop drinking.

What to Expect as the Remedy Works

Like the remedy Aconite (page 168), Stramonium can release the damaging effects of shock and trauma. It frees your energy body of the cramping effects of experiencing fear for your life. The after-shocks of displacement, loss and abandonment can be neutralized by the curative action of Stramonium, if this remedy is the one that is indicated for you. The remedy heals profound anxieties about survival which have been created by traumatic events in your own experience and those of your parents. It will allow you to come to terms with your existential terror. You may have been locked out of fully inhabiting your own body by sheer terror. Your soul needs to incarnate fully as you learn that it is OK to be in your body.

As you feel more secure, fears and phobias of all descriptions subside. Nightmares and bed-wetting clear up. Tics and tremors disappear. As your fear of abandonment diminishes, you feel safe enough to emerge from your reclusive lifestyle. You can relax and take your eyes off the exit sign. You can begin to laugh again, rediscovering the pleasures of being alive.

Soul Learning for Stramonium

Learning to trust that the world is a safe place for you. Experiment with trying to open up to love rather than contracting in fear.

Sulphur

The tremendous energy involved in the Sulphur remedy pattern leads to mental stimulation, in which the person receives a constant flood of ideas. They are engaged with the world on an intellectual level, and excited by what they learn. They are good communicators and enjoy discussion and debate. They can talk easily on a range of subjects, elaborating their theories in some depth. People in this energy pattern are inventive, inspiring others, and they are good philosophers, lateral thinkers and trouble-shooters. They have a philosophical bent, enjoying questioning issues and thinking through matters of life and death.

Because of their awareness of their ability to think about existential issues more profoundly than other people, there is a risk of becoming arrogant and egotistical – only talking about their own ideas. They can find others boring, especially if other people don't listen to them with avid interest. Usually they are ardent, enthusiastic and skilful at convincing and motivating others. They often function well as ideas people, leaving others in the team to get on with practicalities.

People in the Sulphur pattern can have a problem with lack of focus. The flow of ideas through their minds can be overwhelming, and they find it difficult to distinguish the relative merits of different approaches. Sometimes their ideas are vague and lacking in detail because of a dearth of mental clarity.

This difficulty with articulating things means that plans can stay at the germination stage and rarely become projects, or else they are superseded by other plans before they have a chance of being implemented. They can be poor at completing projects because they have already moved on to the next thing in their minds, and they lose patience about having to deal with practical problems. They are easily seduced intellectually, and the next and newest idea seems more interesting than the one they had last week. Others find people in this energy pattern interesting to talk to or bounce thoughts off, but sometimes their suggestions can be too wild or ungrounded.

Sulphur people can be good at initiating things and inspiring others, but it is often a good idea to get someone else on board who is good at seeing things through. All the wonderful potential of their mental activity runs the risk of remaining unfulfilled potential. When other people realize that someone in the Sulphur pattern rarely achieves what they set out to do, they stop listening to their plans. When this happens, the Sulphur person can give in to a feeling of apathy. Even at the best of times they are lazy about the amount of effort it takes to get things going, and they often procrastinate.

The chaos in the thinking of people stuck in the Sulphur pattern leads to dysfunction in other areas of their lives. Relationships suffer. Their sophisticated intellectual function is often at the expense of emotional development. Their lifestyles tend to be chaotic. Because of their interest in the world of ideas, they tend to be less interested in the mundane world. The material aspects of their lives are neglected and their surroundings often untidy, with papers and objects scattered all around.

I once went to see a palmist who had been highly recommended to me. I was struck by the extreme disorder in his flat, with books and objects piled everywhere, on every surface, and glasses containing the dregs of wine left unwashed in several locations around the room. He offered me a glass of wine, talking volubly about his far-fetched thoughts about my future – all of which have proved to be his own fantasies. He had clearly tried his hand at painting the vinyl sofa a lurid orange, and when I visited the bathroom I was amused to find the same colour on the toilet seat and bath surround.

The Sulphur energy pattern is common in people who use cannabis daily. Their brains become permanently foggy and they experience a tremendous feeling of inertia. After a time they become so laid-back they are virtually prostrate, and a lot of creative possibilities are wasted. There is often a toxic residue in the body that builds up over a period of time in this state, and Sulphur as a remedy does a very good job of cleansing the body. Its detox effects can sometimes be quite drastic – the dosage and repetition of this remedy need to be monitored carefully.

Physically, people with the Sulphur remedy pattern tend to suffer from symptoms of irritation, particularly in the skin and bowels. While a large number of other remedies also cover these symptoms, this remedy will clear up such symptoms in a person who resonates with the Sulphur energy pattern.

Phil, who was doing a degree in archaeology, described finding it difficult to concentrate; he felt that his brain was 'foggy'. He said that this problem was aggravated by recurrent sinus trouble, which caused a feeling of 'wool behind my eyes ... I know what I want to say but I can't seem to get my ideas down on paper.' He would go off on long flights of fantasy in which his thoughts seemed very detailed and clear, but when he tried to formulate them afterwards they suddenly seemed intangible.

Phil had used cannabis regularly for over two decades, since his teenage years. As with many cannabis users, his creative potential had been wasted because of tremendous inertia, and his thinking had become less and less focused. Even before this, his health had been ravaged by the use of penicillin in earlier years. Penicillin had produced only temporary relief of his sinus troubles, which had in fact become more frequent and eventually turned into a chronic problem. He also suffered from genital herpes which erupted a few times a year when he was particularly run down. He had already seen a homeopath in the past, who had attempted to treat him with other remedies. But to me, the pattern of intellectual obstruction together with the toxic build-up in his system pointed clearly to the remedy Sulphur, and his first dose produced a dramatic response.

It was only once he experienced how much taking the remedy sharpened his thinking faculties that Phil realized how dulled they had become. He felt much more mentally alert and focused. His sleep was much better, deeper and more refreshing.

He suffered much less frequently from the herpes that had plagued him for several years. The attacks became less intense as well, fading away over the next year.

What to Expect as the Remedy Works

The central action of Sulphur is one of cleansing. It cleanses on every level: mental, emotional and physical. Sometimes the cleansing effects of the remedy can produce quite drastic reactions such as diarrhoea or skin eruptions. Because of the risk of aggravation, the dosage and repetition of this remedy need to be carefully monitored by your homeopath. Such reactions are part of the detoxification process, and eventually Sulphur alleviates any long-term symptoms of digestive disturbance or skin problems. The remedy helps you to be in your own skin, and any inflamed and itchy skin condition that you have clears up. When your body is more comfortable you can inhabit it more easily. Your senses are heightened and you feel rejuvenated and energetic.

The remedy helps your intellectual capacities become more acute; your thought processes become insightful and penetrating. You feel more focused and less distracted by competing ideas. Sulphur will help you to focus and pull your ideas into a coherent shape. It will help you to put your ideas into context and see which are appropriate.

Sulphur spring-cleans your mind, and this will allow you to clear up the clutter of your domestic life. Taking the remedy firms your resolve, enabling you to actualize your potential.

One of the problems created by your ease of lateral thinking is that you can come to assume that you are more creative and interesting than others. Sulphur will cure you of this inflated egotism so that you are sensitive to the contributions of others. The remedy helps you to learn that the world is not just a mirror of your own self. You explore what lies beyond the confines of ego and connect with the spiritual realm.

Soul Learning for Sulphur

Applying your flair for thinking and analysing to develop a deep understanding. You need to uncover a deeper meaning to life and to convert knowledge to wisdom.

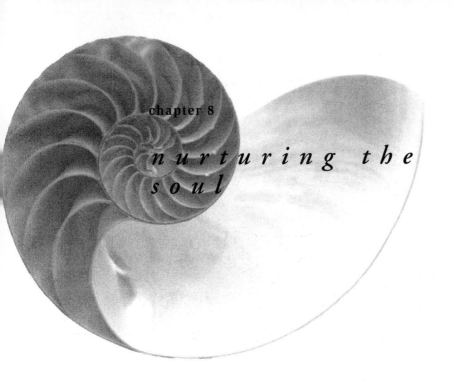

chapter 8

nurturing the soul

Some of the advice I gave in the entries for individual remedies applies to us all, if we are to learn to nurture our souls. All of us need to realize that holding on to unresolved problems, resentments and frustrations just creates armour around our souls and prevents the free flow of energy. Letting go of this armour frees us from the habitual incarcerations of our minds. In letting go of introspective tendencies, we learn to open up to others and trust them again.

One way through the unfinished business of the past is to understand how our own psychological pain is related to previous experiences or patterns of relating within our family. These past experiences have shaped our present responses and therefore determine, to some extent, what we are now going through. We often need to acknowledge the pain of past difficulties and then move on to a more forgiving perspective.

A lack of forgiveness blocks the exchange of energy between ourselves and others, so that we feel separate from other people. Forgiveness allows a connection and re-establishes interchange. In order to forgive, we need to go into the emotional softness of compassion rather than remain in the hardness of judgement. Compassion is what converts the feeling of anger into one of mercy. This happens when we allow our hearts to open towards others. Homeopathic remedies enable us to feel more loving compassion both for ourselves and others, thus healing the wounds of the past and present. We need to resolve to live more fully in each and every moment rather than hang on to the incomplete past or armour ourselves against the present.

I make a distinction between feelings and emotions. Feelings arise as a result of what is happening in the present moment, while emotions are usually to do with past situations. Remedies help us to let go of stuck emotions and experience the feelings that are appropriate to our current situations. They allow us to let go of the negative emotions that sap our energy, and they encourage joy and laughter, the feelings that nurture us.

We need to trust in the greater wisdom of the universe, for we cannot always understand why things happen to us. Finding the courage to move on allows us to open up to new experiences.

Love is the key lesson for all the remedies. When our energy is blocked, our hearts feel heavy and sad, and we are unable to open up to relationships. When our energy is flowing freely again, we are more able to be in the present. We can then experience the small gifts of love that are present in our everyday interactions. We can also experience the deeper feelings of love and compassion that are part of our existential reality, if we can only tune in to it.

Ways to Nurture Your Soul

Homeopathy is not only of use when we have profound emotional problems or troubling physical symptoms. We can also use the principles of homeopathy to treat energy blocks before they create knots and serious problems develop. Homeopathic treatment is perfect for stimulating energy and creating equilibrium within our energy body.

We also need to find ways of nurturing our souls before problems occur. An important part of feeling fulfilled is finding meaning and a sense of purpose in life, but this does not mean that we have to be deadly serious and earnest about it.

We tend to defer our happiness, and we endlessly put off the task of sorting things out in our lives. But the longer we do this, the more we become identified with a negative state, and the harder it is to rid ourselves of that state. We need to prioritize our own happiness and ensure that fun and pleasure are built into all our activities, even work. We need to change our attitudes and our habits so that we can get more out of what we are doing.

These are some of the things you can do to nurture your soul:

- Make time for the sacred through prayer, meditation or contemplation.
- Be aware of your breathing: to deepen your breath allow yourself to take in more oxygen, and exhale slowly.
- Have periods of quiet time every day: try walking, sitting, meditating or yoga.
- Explore your creativity by singing, dancing, drawing, writing or making things.
- Connect with others. When you are with friends, really look at them and listen to what they are saying. Respond to them.
- Develop a loving heart. Put up a photo of someone you love, and spend a few minutes each day gazing at it, feeling your heart open. Concentrate on your heart opening when you are with those you love.
- Honour sex: it is a means of bringing yourself into a deeply loving connection.
- Give to others. Service is important, so make an effort to do things without being asked.

- Develop compassion through understanding, accepting and loving yourself and others, regardless of your or their faults.
- Practise forgiveness; let go of the past.
- Switch off your mind, and try not to pay attention to the critical voice in your head.
- Accept things as they are; practise observing without judgement.
- Learn to receive. Allow yourself to accept what others offer you.
- Value integrity: check that your actions are congruent with your beliefs.
- Foster a sense of purpose. Ask yourself regularly, 'what is it I really want to do?'
- Learn to look after the needs of your body; it is the vehicle of your soul.
- Pay attention to illness: symptoms are telling you that there is something wrong in your life that needs changing.
- Be sceptical about conventional medicine: it is your energy body that needs re-balancing – suppressing the symptoms will do no good in the long term.
- Take a sabbatical; even a holiday can help you to re-evaluate your life.
- Make time for your genius. Make sure you nurture your talents: they are the voice of your soul.
- Manifest your vision: it is important to ground your ideals in your work.

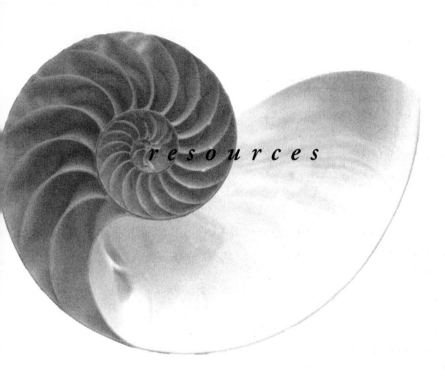
resources

Finding a Homeopath

Your local homeopathic pharmacy can advise you on practitioners in your area.

UK

A register of trained homeopaths in the UK is available from:

THE SOCIETY OF HOMEOPATHS

2 Artizan Road
Northampton NN1 4HU
01604 621400

For a list of medically trained homeopaths:

FACULTY OF HOMEOPATHY
15 Clerkenwell Close
London EC1R 0AA
020 7566 7810

BRITISH HOMEOPATHIC ASSOCIATION
15 Clerkenwell Close
London EC1R 0AA
020 7566 7800

USA

NATIONAL CENTER FOR HOMEOPATHY
1500 Massachusetts Ave N.W.
Suite 42
Washington, DC 20005
(202) 223 6182

AMERICAN INSTITUTE OF HOMEOPATHY
801 N Fairfax Street
Suite 306
Alexandria
VA 22314
(703) 246 9501

Australia

MARTIN & PLEASANCE
PO Box 4
Collingwood
Victoria 3066
(61341) 99733

further reading

Biddulph, Steve. *The Secret of Happy Children* (Bay Books, 1984; Thorsons, 1998)

Castro, Miranda. *Stress* (Macmillan, 1994)

Chappell, Peter. *Emotional Healing with Homeopathy* (Element Books, 1994)

Coulter, Catherine. *Portraits of Homeopathic Medicines* (North Atlantic Books, 1986)

Chopra, Deepak. *The Path to Love* (Harmony Books, 1997)

Dalai Lama and Howard Cutler. *The Art of Happiness* (Hodder and Stoughton, 1998)

Dalai Lama, His Holiness the. *Healing Anger* (Snow Lion, 1997)

Dowrick, Stephanie. *Forgiveness and Other Acts of Love* (Viking/Penguin, 1997)

Greenwood, Dr M. and P. Nunn. *The Paradox of Healing* (Prion, 1996)

Harvey, Andrew. *The Direct Path* (Random House, 2000)

Hillman, James. *The Soul's Code* (Bantam Books, 1996)

Le Shan, Lawrence. *Cancer as a Turning Point* (Dutton, 1989)

Levine, Stephen. *Healing into Life and Death* (Gateway Books, 1987)

Miles, Martin. *Homeopathy and Human Evolution* (Winter Press, 1992)

Myss, Caroline. *Anatomy of the Spirit* (Bantam Books, 1996)

   –. *Why People Don't Heal and How They Can* (Harmony, 1997)

Pert, Candace. *Molecules of Emotion* (Scribner, 1997)

Rumi, Jalal-a-din. *The Path of Love* (trans Camille and Kabir Helminski; Element
   Books, 1999)

Sankaran, Rajan. *The Spirit of Homeopathy* (Bombay, 1991)

Vithoulkas, George. *The Science of Homeopathy* (Grove Press, 1980)

Whitmont, Edward and Sylvia Brinton Perera. *Dreams: A Portal to the Source*
   (Routledge, 1989)

Whitmont, Edward. *Psyche and Substance* (North Atlantic Books, 1982)

Zaren, Ananda. *Core Elements of the Materia Medica of the Mind* (Gottingen:
   Burgdorf Homeopathic Publishing House, 1993)

index

Aconitum napellus 168–71
    shock 109, 142, 156–7, 168–71
    trauma 168–71
Addiction 50–51, 74–8, 203–4
    to alcohol 32
    to drugs 74–5, 203–4
    to food 35
    to medicines 82
    to sex 80–81
Agaricus 84
Aggravation of symptoms xxii, 32, 41, 100
Altruism 52, 60, 187
Alumina 92, 103
Ambra grisea 135
Anacardium 81, 92, 103, 115, 118, 124,
    171–5
    compassion 171–5
    conflict 174

    conscience 174
Anger 78–82, 141, 161, 173, 175, 186, 201,
    211
    about exploitation 31
    about injustice 62
    about powerlessness 91
    about sexual abuse 152, 153
    post-natal 111, 137
    righteous anger 190
Anxiety 78–82, 82–5
    of conscience (guilt) 117
    about health 23, 82, 94, 99, 141, 175–6
    about others 53
    obsessional 28
    separation 7, 108
    sexual 11
Apis 127
Argentum nitricum 36, 84, 142

Arnica 157
Arsenicum album 11, 83–4, 121, 138, 143,
        175–80
    arthritis 29
    bladder infection 114
    depression 94, 178
    kidney infection 114
    perfectionism 138
    orgasm 114, 177
Asarum 121
Aurum metallicum 60, 111, 115, 180–84
    death 96
    loss 130, 132
Avena sativa 77

Baryta carbonica 27, 124, 135, 160
Belladonna 109
Berberis 33
Bryonia 46, 81,162
Bufo 153
Burnout 85–9

Caladium 153
Calcarea carbonica 54, 92, 135, 137, 148,
        184–7
    lack of energy 31, 160, 184–7
    patience 187
Calcarea phosphorica 112
Cannabis indica 120
Capsicum 77
Carbo vegetablis 139
Carcinocin 103
Causticum 14, 62, 81, 100–01, 139, 187–90
    authority 5, 188
    disillusionment 5
    idealism 187–90
    spirituality 5, 188
Chamomilla 81
Chelidonium 118
China officinalis 32, 96, 112, 121
Cimicifuga 96
Classical homeopathy 21
Cocculus 88, 106, 30

Coffea 121
Confusion 89–93
Conium 112, 153
Constitutional remedy xvii, 17–18, 69, 98,
        167
Conventional medicine 22, 39, 98, 105
Cyclamen 103, 130
Depression 93–7
    manic depression 79, 215
Digitalis 118
Disease 97–102
Drosera 112
Dulcamara 146

Emptiness 34–5, 74, 102–4, 218, 220

Fatigue 104–7
Fear 107–10, 215
    of being alone 80, 109, 128, 235
    of chaos 83, 180
    of cancer 84
    of contamination 83, 84, 109, 119,
        126, 177
    of dark 108, 109, 157, 235
    of dying 23, 28, 109, 155, 171, 176
    of fear (panic) 140
    of poverty 84
Feeling trapped 110–12
Fluoric acid 153
Forgiveness 113–15, 242

Gelsemium 84, 88, 106
Graphites 92, 124
Grief 130–33
Guilt 116–19

Hahnemann, Samuel xii
Healing, laws of 21, 26–32, 32–3
Helleborus 90–92, 105–6
Hepar sulphur 81
Homeopathic consultation xiii, 16–18
Homeopathic treatment 74
Hura 130

Hyosycamus 127, 154
Hypersensitivity 119–22

Ignatia 149, 190–95
    disappointment 121, 190–95
    grief 96, 132, 190–95
Internal conflict 122–4
Iodum 84

Jealousy 125–7

Kali arsenicum 141
Kali bromatum 119, 149, 154
Kali carbonica 103
Kali phosphorica 106

Lac caninum 19, 135
Lachesis 19, 195–8
    anger 196–8
    jealousy 126, 196, 198
    sex 196–8
Leuticum 84, 119
Lilium tigrinum 96, 127
Loneliness 127–30
Loss 130–33
Low self-esteem 133–6
Lycopodium 139, 146, 154, 199–203
    confidence 151, 159, 199–202
    courage 202
    humiliation 202
    power 202
    will 203

Mancinella 109
Medorrhinum 32, 81, 98, 139, 149, 154,
    203–6
    addiction 76, 203–4, 206
    creativity 206
    integrity 203, 206
Mercurius solubilis 12, 96
Moschus 81, 139
Muriatic acid 88, 106

Natrum carbonicum 135
Natrum muriaticum 10, 13, 58, 94–5, 119,
    132, 149–50, 153, 206–11
    betrayal 115, 210
    forgiveness 207, 210
    resentment 115, 133, 207–10
Natrum sulphuricum 96
Nitric acid 34, 81, 115
Nitrous oxide 77
Nux moschata 77
Nux vomica 77, 211–14
    action 49
    anger 80–81, 152, 161, 211–13

Onosmodium 154
Opium 77
Oppression 136–40
Origanon 154

Palladium 144–5
Panic Attacks 84, 140–43, 156
Phosphoric acid 88
Phosphorus 65, 87, 109, 122, 214–17
    ego
    empathy 214, 217
    grounding 215–17
Picric acid 106
Platina 104, 145
Plumbum 92
Pride 143–6
Psorinum 84, 130, 162
Pulsatilla 56, 96, 109, 123–4, 129, 139,
    156, 217–21
    abandonment 7, 71, 218–20

Relationship problems 146–50
Remedies 15
    response to 21, 26–32
    taking of 24–5
    timing of taking 41
Rhus toxicodendron 84

Selenium 106
Sepia 88, 96, 221–5
    hormones 111, 223–5
    service 226
Sexual problems 150–54
Shock 154–7
Silica 85, 107, 124, 136, 226–30
    sensitivity 226–30
    trust 226, 230
Spiritual searching 45, 102
Stagnation in work 158–60
Stannum 88, 107
Staphysagria 9, 157, 230–4
    abuse 231
    boundaries 231, 233–4
    frustration 230–31
    love 55, 150, 154, 231
Stramonium 234–7
    loneliness 130

phobias 235, 237
    terror 108, 143, 157, 234–7
Stress 78, 106, 211, 213
Sulphur 34, 77, 92, 102, 146, 237–40
    cleansing 239
    wisdom 67, 240
Sulphuric acid 122

Tarentula hispanica 85, 127, 137, 162
Theridion 122
Thuja 30, 98, 124, 140
    guilt 118

Veratrum 127, 146
Vithoulkas, George xvi, 17

Workaholism 160–62

Zincum metallicum 112